M337 Unit A3
Mathematics: A Third Level Course

COMPLEX ANALYSIS

UNIT A3 CONTINUITY

Prepared by the Course Team

PLEX ANALYSIS COMPLEX ANALYSIS COMPL

Before working through this text, make sure that you have read the
Course Guide for M337 Complex Analysis.

The Open University, Walton Hall, Milton Keynes, MK7 6AA.

First published 1993. Reprinted 1995, 1998, 2001, 2008

Edited, designed and typeset by the Open University using the Open University T$_E$X System.

Printed in Malta by Gutenberg Press Limited.

ISBN 0 7492 2177 1

This text forms part of an Open University Third Level Course. If you would like a copy of
Studying with The Open University, please write to the Central Enquiry Service,
PO Box 200, The Open University, Walton Hall, Milton Keynes, MK7 6YZ. If you have not
already enrolled on the Course and would like to buy this or other Open University material,
please write to Open University Educational Enterprises Ltd, 12 Cofferidge Close, Stony
Stratford, Milton Keynes, MK11 1BY, United Kingdom.

1.4

CONTENTS

INTRODUCTION

In *Unit A2* we introduced complex functions and began to study the way in which they map subsets of $\mathbb{C}$ to $\mathbb{C}$. In this unit we look more closely at such functions and prove that many of them have the property of being *continuous*.

Roughly speaking, a function is continuous if it always maps nearby points in the domain to nearby points in the codomain. More precisely, this means that any convergent sequence $z_1, z_2, z_3, \ldots$, with limit α, say, in the domain is mapped by the continuous function f to a convergent sequence $f(z_1), f(z_2), f(z_3), \ldots$, with limit $f(\alpha)$, in the codomain, as indicated in Figure 0.1.

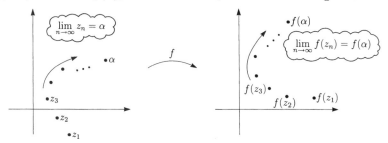

Figure 0.1

Continuity is important in complex analysis because, in many cases, the easiest way to *prove* that a given function has a certain property is to use the fact that the function is continuous. For example, to show that a given polynomial function p is such that $|p(z)|$ has a maximum value on the closed disc $\{z : |z| \leq 1\}$, we make use of the fact that p is continuous and appeal to a general result concerning continuous functions called the Extreme Value Theorem, from which it follows that such a maximum *exists*. To approach this problem by trying to *calculate* the maximum value of $|p(z)|$ on the disc is, in general, a difficult task.

For example,
$p(z) = z^{20} + z^3 - 1$.

In Section 1 we define the notion of a *convergent sequence* and describe many properties of such sequences. We also discuss divergent sequences. In Section 2 (the audio-tape section) we use this notion of a convergent sequence to define a *continuous function* in the way described above. We then give several rules which state, for example, that *combinations of continuous functions are continuous*, and that *composites of continuous functions are continuous*. Using these rules, together with a list of *basic* continuous functions, we can show that most of the functions introduced so far are continuous.

In Section 3 we define the *limit of a function*, a notion which is closely related to continuity; this will be an essential tool in *Unit A4* when we come to discuss differentiability of complex functions.

In Sections 4 and 5 we discuss different types of subsets of $\mathbb{C}$ which we will need throughout the course: *open sets, connected sets, regions, closed sets, bounded sets* and *compact sets*.

Study guide

This unit introduces many basic concepts which are essential tools in the study of complex analysis and it also contains a larger than average number of proofs. Many of these proofs are short, but some are rather tricky, and we have tried to ease your study by indicating those proofs which may be omitted on a first reading. Once you are quite familiar with all the basic concepts, it should be much easier for you to follow these proofs.

Associated with this unit is a segment of the Video Tape for the course. Although this unit text is self-contained, access to the video tape will enhance your understanding. Suitable points at which to view the video tape are indicated by a symbol placed in the margin.

1 SEQUENCES

After working through this section, you should be able to:

(a) explain the statement 'the sequence $\{z_n\}$ is convergent with limit α';

(b) recognize certain *basic null sequences*;

(c) show that a sequence is null by working from the definition, and by using the Squeeze Rule;

(d) use the Combination Rules to calculate the limits of sequences;

(e) explain the statement 'the sequence $\{z_n\}$ tends to infinity';

(f) use the Subsequence Rules to recognize *divergent sequences*.

1.1 Convergent sequences

Ever since learning to count, you have been familiar with the sequence of natural numbers

$$1, 2, 3, 4, 5, 6, \dots.$$

You will have also encountered many other sequences of numbers, such as

$$1, 3, 5, 7, 9, 11, \dots,$$
$$\frac{1}{2}, \frac{1}{4}, \frac{1}{8}, \frac{1}{16}, \frac{1}{32}, \frac{1}{64}, \dots.$$

In this section we study sequences of *complex* numbers. We begin with a definition and some notation.

Definitions A (**complex**) **sequence** is an unending list of complex numbers

$$z_1, z_2, z_3, \dots.$$

The complex number z_n is called the **nth term of the sequence** and the sequence is denoted by $\{z_n\}$.

Note that a real sequence is a particular type of complex sequence.

A sequence is usually defined by stating an explicit formula for the nth term. This can be done in more than one way. For example, the expression $\{2n + i\}$ denotes the sequence

$$2 + i, 4 + i, 6 + i, 8 + i, \dots,$$

as does

$$z_n = 2n + i, \qquad n = 1, 2, \dots.$$

It is often helpful to picture how a given sequence behaves by plotting the first few terms in the complex plane; two examples are shown in Figures 1.1 and 1.2.

The sequences specified in this definition and exemplified below all have first term z_1. Sometimes it is convenient or necessary to start with a term other than z_1. For example, the sequence

$$z_n = \frac{i}{n^2 - 1}, \qquad n = 2, 3, \dots$$

begins with z_2 and could be written $\{z_n\}_2^\infty$.

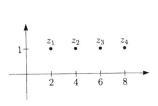

Figure 1.1 $z_n = 2n + i, \quad n = 1, 2, \dots$

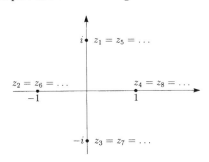

Figure 1.2 $z_n = i^n, \quad n = 1, 2, \dots$

The first eight terms of the sequence $\{i^n\}$ are

$$i, -1, -i, 1, i, -1, -i, 1.$$

5

Problem 1.1 _____

Plot the first four terms of each of the following sequences.

(a) $\{i/n\}$ (b) $\{1/n + in\}$ (c) $\{(2i)^n\}$

_____

The terms of the sequence illustrated in Figure 1.1 lie on the line $y = 1$ and march out to the right as n increases; the terms of the sequence in Figure 1.2 go round and round the origin (on the circle $|z| = 1$) as n increases. These sequences do not appear to be convergent; that is, as n gets larger and larger they do not settle down near any fixed point of $\mathbb{C}$. By contrast, consider the sequence

$$z_n = (0.9i)^n, \qquad n = 1, 2, \ldots,$$

whose few terms (correct to 2 significant figures)

n	1	2	3	4	5	6	7	8
z_n	$0.9i$	-0.81	$-0.73i$	0.66	$0.59i$	-0.53	$-0.48i$	0.43

are plotted in Figure 1.3. From this diagram we observe that the sequence $\{z_n\}$ spirals around the origin getting closer and closer to it. Indeed, it seems likely that we can make the terms as close as we please to 0 by taking n large enough. More precisely, no matter how small an open disc centered on the origin we consider, the terms of the sequence $\{z_n\}$ will eventually lie inside the disc. For example, if we take the radius of the disc to be 0.6, then

$$|z_n| < 0.6, \qquad \text{for all } n > 4.$$

More generally, it appears that for each radius $\varepsilon > 0$, there is an integer N such that

$$|z_n| < \varepsilon, \qquad \text{for all } n > N. \tag{$*$}$$

We shall prove this statement later in the section — see Theorem 1.2(b).

In fact, the statement $(*)$ gives a precise definition of what it means for a sequence $\{z_n\}$ to be convergent, with limit 0. Moreover, this statement may be readily adapted to give a precise definition of what it means for a given sequence $\{z_n\}$ to be convergent, with limit α: the terms of $\{z_n\}$ must eventually lie in any open disc, centred at α, no matter how small its radius.

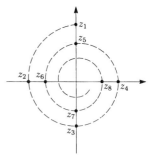

Figure 1.3 $z_n = (0.9i)^n$

The Greek lower case letter ε (epsilon) is commonly used to denote a small positive number.

Note the convenient use of the word 'eventually' to mean 'for all but a finite number of values of n'.

Definitions   The sequence $\{z_n\}$ is **convergent with limit α**, or **converges to α**, or **tends to α**, if

for each positive number ε, there is an integer N such that

$$|z_n - \alpha| < \varepsilon, \qquad \text{for all } n > N.$$

(Figure 1.4 illustrates this definition.)

If $\{z_n\}$ converges to α, then we write

EITHER $\lim\limits_{n \to \infty} z_n = \alpha$

OR $z_n \to \alpha$ as $n \to \infty$.

If the limit α is 0, then $\{z_n\}$ is called a **null sequence**.

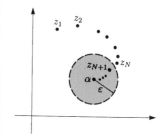

Figure 1.4

Remarks

1 '$\lim\limits_{n \to \infty} z_n = \alpha$' is read as 'the limit of z_n as n tends to infinity is (equal to) α';

'$z_n \to \alpha$ as $n \to \infty$' is read as 'z_n tends to α as n tends to infinity'.

2 The sequence $\{z_n\}$ converges to α if and only if the sequence $\{z_n - \alpha\}$ is null (or, equivalently, if and only if the real sequence $\{|z_n - \alpha|\}$ is null).

3 If a sequence $\{z_n\}$ is convergent, then it has a *unique* limit. For, if $\{z_n\}$ has limits α and β with $\alpha \neq \beta$ and if we put $\varepsilon = \frac{1}{3}|\alpha - \beta|$, then the open discs

$$\{z : |z - \alpha| < \varepsilon\} \qquad \text{and} \qquad \{z : |z - \beta| < \varepsilon\}$$

do not overlap (Figure 1.5), and the terms z_n cannot eventually lie in both discs.

4 A sequence $\{z_n\}$ is **constant** if $z_{n+1} = z_n$, for $n = 1, 2, \ldots$.

The constant sequence

$$z_n = \alpha, \qquad n = 1, 2, \ldots$$

is convergent with limit α.

5 If a given sequence converges to α, then this remains true if we *add, delete, or alter a finite number of terms*.

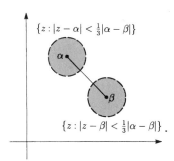

$\{z : |z - \alpha| < \frac{1}{3}|\alpha - \beta|\}$

$\{z : |z - \beta| < \frac{1}{3}|\alpha - \beta|\}$.

Figure 1.5

In other words, 'a finite number of terms doesn't matter'.

You will need to be familiar with techniques for finding limits of convergent sequences. First we give examples of simple null sequences and then we discuss rules for dealing with more complicated sequences.

Example 1.1

Prove that the sequence $\{i/n\}$ is null.

Solution

We want to show that

for each positive number ε, there is an integer N such that

$$\left|\frac{i}{n}\right| < \varepsilon, \qquad \text{for all } n > N. \tag{$*$}$$

But $|i/n| = 1/n$ and we know that

$$\frac{1}{n} < \varepsilon \quad \Longleftrightarrow \quad n > \frac{1}{\varepsilon}.$$

Therefore the statement $(*)$ would be true if we could take $N = 1/\varepsilon$. However, $1/\varepsilon$ is not necessarily an integer, so instead we take $N = [1/\varepsilon]$, the integer part of $1/\varepsilon$. Then if $n > N$, we must have $n > 1/\varepsilon$ (since n is also an integer) so that $1/n < \varepsilon$. Thus

$$\frac{1}{n} < \varepsilon, \qquad \text{for all } n > N = [1/\varepsilon],$$

as required. Hence $\{i/n\}$ is a null sequence. ∎

For example, if $\varepsilon = 0.12$ then
$$N = [1/\varepsilon] = \left[8\tfrac{1}{3}\right] = 8,$$
and so
$$\frac{1}{n} < 0.12, \qquad \text{for all } n > 8.$$

Note that, in this solution and in general, the integer N becomes larger as the positive number ε becomes smaller, as you would expect.

Problem 1.2

Prove that each of the following sequences is null.

(a) $\{1/\sqrt{n}\}$ (b) $\{(1+i)/n\}$

Proving that a sequence is null from the definition, as illustrated above, is quite tricky. We now introduce a result which enables us to avoid using the definition in many cases. Consider, for example, the sequence

$$z_n = \frac{i^n}{1 + \sqrt{n}}, \qquad n = 1, 2, \ldots.$$

From Figure 1.6 it seems clear that $\{z_n\}$ is a null sequence and further evidence for this is provided by the inequality

$$|z_n| = \left| \frac{i^n}{1 + \sqrt{n}} \right| = \frac{|i|^n}{1 + \sqrt{n}} = \frac{1}{1 + \sqrt{n}} \leq \frac{1}{\sqrt{n}}, \qquad (1.1)$$

which shows that $|z_n|$ is squeezed between 0 and $1/\sqrt{n}$. Since we know that the sequence $\{1/\sqrt{n}\}$ is null (by Problem 1.2(a)), it seems likely that $\{z_n\}$ must be null also. This is confirmed by the Squeeze Rule.

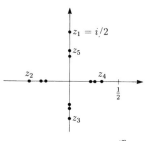

Figure 1.6 $z_n = \dfrac{i^n}{1 + \sqrt{n}}$

Theorem 1.1 Squeeze Rule

If $\{a_n\}$ is a real null sequence of non-negative terms, and if

$$|z_n| \leq a_n, \qquad \text{for } n = 1, 2, \ldots,$$

then $\{z_n\}$ is a null sequence.

Note that $|z_n|$ and a_n are real and non-negative for each n.

Proof   We want to show that

for each positive number ε, there is an integer N such that

$$|z_n| < \varepsilon, \qquad \text{for all } n > N. \qquad (*)$$

But, since $\{a_n\}$ is null, there is an integer N such that

$$a_n < \varepsilon, \qquad \text{for all } n > N.$$

Hence, with this value of N,

$$|z_n| \leq a_n < \varepsilon, \qquad \text{for all } n > N,$$

and so $(*)$ does indeed hold.   ∎

Remember $a_n \geq 0$, so that $|a_n| = a_n$.

When the inequality

$$|z_n| \leq a_n$$

holds for $n = 1, 2, \ldots$ (or even for all but a finite number of terms of the sequence), we say that the real sequence $\{a_n\}$ **dominates** the sequence $\{z_n\}$ (Figure 1.7). For example, we saw in Inequality (1.1) that the sequence

$$z_n = i^n/(1 + \sqrt{n}), \qquad n = 1, 2, \ldots$$

is dominated by the known null sequence

$$a_n = 1/\sqrt{n}, \qquad n = 1, 2, \ldots;$$

thus $\{z_n\}$ is null by the Squeeze Rule. This illustrates the *strategy* for using the Squeeze Rule — we suspect that $\{z_n\}$ is null, and we prove it by choosing a suitable dominating null sequence. We ask you to apply this strategy in the following problem.

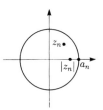

Figure 1.7
$\{a_n\}$ dominates $\{z_n\}$

Problem 1.3

(a) Prove that

$$z_n = \frac{(0.6 + 0.8i)^n}{n^2 + n}, \qquad n = 1, 2, \ldots,$$

is a null sequence.
   (*Hint:*   First calculate $|0.6 + 0.8i|$.)

(b) Use the inequality $2^n \geq n$, for $n = 1, 2, \ldots$, (which can be proved by Mathematical Induction) to prove that $\{(i/2)^n\}$ is a null sequence.

We now give two types of basic null sequences.

Theorem 1.2 Basic Null Sequences

The following sequences are null.

(a) $\left\{ \dfrac{1}{n^p} \right\}$,   for $p > 0$.

(b) $\{\alpha^n\}$,   for $|\alpha| < 1$.

The proof of Theorem 1.2 appears in Subsection 1.3.

For example, $p = \frac{1}{2}$ gives $\left\{ \dfrac{1}{\sqrt{n}} \right\}$; $\alpha = 0.9i$ gives $\{(0.9i)^n\}$, which provides a proof promised earlier.

Using these basic null sequences, it is possible to deduce the convergence of many sequences. For example, if

$$z_n = 1 + \left(\tfrac{1}{2}i\right)^n, \qquad n = 1, 2, \ldots,$$

then

$$z_n - 1 = \left(\tfrac{1}{2}i\right)^n, \qquad n = 1, 2, \ldots.$$

Since $\left\{ \left(\tfrac{1}{2}i\right)^n \right\}$ is a basic null sequence (because $\left|\tfrac{1}{2}i\right| = \tfrac{1}{2} < 1$), the sequence $\{z_n\}$ is convergent with limit $\alpha = 1$ (by Remark 2). Usually, however, it is not so easy to recognize the limit of a sequence (when this exists). Instead, we may try to apply the following Combination Rules for convergent sequences.

Theorem 1.3 Combination Rules

If $\lim\limits_{n \to \infty} z_n = \alpha$ and $\lim\limits_{n \to \infty} w_n = \beta$, then

Sum Rule $\lim\limits_{n \to \infty} (z_n + w_n) = \alpha + \beta$;

Multiple Rule $\lim\limits_{n \to \infty} (\lambda z_n) = \lambda \alpha$,   where $\lambda \in \mathbb{C}$;

Product Rule $\lim\limits_{n \to \infty} (z_n w_n) = \alpha \beta$;

Quotient Rule $\lim\limits_{n \to \infty} \left(\dfrac{z_n}{w_n} \right) = \dfrac{\alpha}{\beta}$,   provided that $\beta \neq 0$.

The proof of Theorem 1.3 appears in Subsection 1.3.

'The limit of the sum is the sum of the limits' etc.

Remarks

1 In applications of the Quotient Rule, it may happen that some of the terms w_n take the value 0, in which case z_n/w_n is not defined. We shall see, however, in the proof of Theorem 1.3, that this can happen for only finitely many w_n (since $\beta \neq 0$), and so w_n is *eventually* non-zero.

A finite number of terms doesn't matter.

2 A special case of the Quotient Rule occurs when

$$z_n = 1, \qquad n = 1, 2, \ldots,$$

and $\lim\limits_{n \to \infty} w_n = \beta$, where $\beta \neq 0$. In this case we deduce that

$$\lim_{n \to \infty} \frac{1}{w_n} = \frac{1}{\beta}.$$

This is sometimes referred to as the *Reciprocal Rule*.

We reserve the label 'Reciprocal Rule' for a related result which appears later.

The following example illustrates how the Combination Rules are used, together with the basic null sequences in Theorem 1.2, to obtain the limits of more complicated sequences.

Example 1.2

Show that each of the following sequences is convergent and find its limit.

(a) $z_n = \dfrac{i}{n} + \left(\dfrac{1+i}{2}\right)^n, \qquad n = 1, 2, \ldots$

(b) $z_n = \dfrac{2in^2 + 3n + 2i}{3n^2 + in}, \qquad n = 1, 2, \ldots$

(c) $z_n = \dfrac{6(1+i)^n + (3+2i)^n}{i(1+5i)^n + (1+i)^n}, \qquad n = 1, 2, \ldots$

Solution

(a) Since $\{1/n\}$ and $\{((1+i)/2)^n\}$ are basic null sequences, we deduce by the Sum and Multiple Rules that

$$\left|\dfrac{1+i}{2}\right| = \dfrac{\sqrt{2}}{2} < 1$$

$$\lim_{n\to\infty} \left(\dfrac{i}{n} + \left(\dfrac{1+i}{2}\right)^n\right) = i \lim_{n\to\infty} \dfrac{1}{n} + \lim_{n\to\infty} \left(\dfrac{1+i}{2}\right)^n$$
$$= (i \times 0) + 0 = 0.$$

(b) Although z_n is expressed as a quotient, we cannot apply the Quotient Rule immediately, because the sequences $\{2in^2 + 3n + 2i\}$ and $\{3n^2 + in\}$ do not appear to be convergent. Instead we rearrange the quotient in such a way that the Combination Rules can be applied. Dividing both the numerator and denominator by n^2, the highest power of n in the numerator or denominator, we obtain

We call n^2 the 'dominant term'.

$$z_n = \dfrac{2in^2 + 3n + 2i}{3n^2 + in} = \dfrac{2i + 3/n + 2i/n^2}{3 + i/n}.$$

Since $\{1/n\}$ is a basic null sequence, we find, by the Combination Rules, that

$$\lim_{n\to\infty} z_n = \dfrac{2i + 0 + 0}{3 + 0} = \dfrac{2}{3}i.$$

(c) Because $|1 + 5i| = \sqrt{26}$, $|3 + 2i| = \sqrt{13}$ and $|1 + i| = \sqrt{2}$, the dominant term is $(1 + 5i)^n$, and so we divide both the numerator and the denominator of z_n by $(1 + 5i)^n$ to obtain

$$z_n = \dfrac{6(1+i)^n + (3+2i)^n}{i(1+5i)^n + (1+i)^n}$$
$$= \dfrac{6((1+i)/(1+5i))^n + ((3+2i)/(1+5i))^n}{i + ((1+i)/(1+5i))^n}.$$

Since

$$|(1+i)/(1+5i)| = \sqrt{2}/\sqrt{26} < 1$$

and

$$|(3+2i)/(1+5i)| = \sqrt{13}/\sqrt{26} < 1,$$

we know that $\{((1+i)/(1+5i))^n\}$ and $\{((3+2i)/(1+5i))^n\}$ are basic null sequences. Hence, by the Combination Rules,

$$\lim_{n\to\infty} z_n = \dfrac{(6 \times 0) + 0}{i + 0} = 0. \quad \blacksquare$$

Remark Note the convenient use of the phrase 'by the Combination Rules' in Example 1.2(b) and (c) when several of these rules are being used.

Problem 1.4

Show that each of the following sequences is convergent and find its limit.

(a) $z_n = \dfrac{n^3 + 2in^2 + 3}{in^3 + 1}, \qquad n = 1, 2, \ldots$

(b) $z_n = \dfrac{(3+i)^n + (2+2i)^n}{(1+2i)^n + 2(3+i)^n}, \qquad n = 1, 2, \ldots$

We end this subsection with a result about convergent sequences which will be useful in Section 2.

Theorem 1.4 If $\displaystyle\lim_{n \to \infty} z_n = \alpha$, then

(a) $\displaystyle\lim_{n \to \infty} |z_n| = |\alpha|$;

(b) $\displaystyle\lim_{n \to \infty} \overline{z_n} = \overline{\alpha}$;

(c) $\displaystyle\lim_{n \to \infty} \operatorname{Re} z_n = \operatorname{Re} \alpha$;

(d) $\displaystyle\lim_{n \to \infty} \operatorname{Im} z_n = \operatorname{Im} \alpha$.

Figure 1.8 illustrates these results.

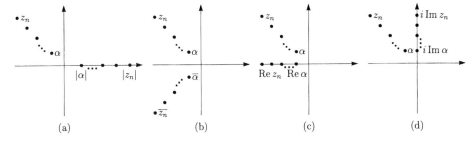

(a)   (b)   (c)   (d)

Figure 1.8

Proof

(a) Since $\displaystyle\lim_{n \to \infty} z_n = \alpha$, we know that $\{|z_n - \alpha|\}$ is a null sequence with non-negative terms. By the backwards form of the Triangle Inequality,

$$\big||z_n| - |\alpha|\big| \le |z_n - \alpha|, \qquad \text{for } n = 1, 2, \ldots,$$

Theorem 5.1, *Unit A1*

so that $\{|z_n| - |\alpha|\}$ is also a null sequence, by the Squeeze Rule. Hence $\displaystyle\lim_{n \to \infty} |z_n| = |\alpha|$, as required.

The proofs of parts (b), (c), (d), which employ the following results, are similar:

These results follow from Theorem 2.1(b) and Inequalities (5.1) of *Unit A1*.

(b) $|\overline{z_n} - \overline{\alpha}| = |\overline{z_n - \alpha}| = |z_n - \alpha|$;

(c) $|\operatorname{Re} z_n - \operatorname{Re} \alpha| = |\operatorname{Re}(z_n - \alpha)| \le |z_n - \alpha|$;

(d) $|\operatorname{Im} z_n - \operatorname{Im} \alpha| = |\operatorname{Im}(z_n - \alpha)| \le |z_n - \alpha|$.   ∎

Problem 1.5

Prove that if $\{x_n\}$ and $\{y_n\}$ are real sequences with $\displaystyle\lim_{n \to \infty} x_n = a$ and $\displaystyle\lim_{n \to \infty} y_n = b$, then $\displaystyle\lim_{n \to \infty} (x_n + iy_n) = a + ib$.

This result is the converse of Theorem 1.4, (c) and (d).

Draw a diagram to illustrate your result.

1.2 Divergent sequences

Having commented earlier that some sequences appear not to be convergent, we now discuss such sequences in more detail.

Definition A sequence which is not convergent is **divergent**.

Figures 1.9 and 1.10 show two sequences which appear to be divergent.

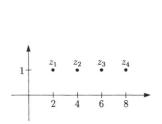

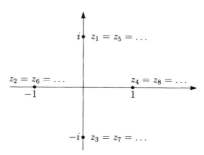

Figure 1.9 $z_n = 2n + i, \quad n = 1, 2, \ldots$ ***Figure 1.10*** $z_n = i^n, \quad n = 1, 2, \ldots$

The sequence $\{2n + i\}$ is divergent because it does not settle down near any fixed point in $\mathbb{C}$. The sequence $\{i^n\}$ makes a better attempt at converging, since the terms at least remain in the closed disc $\{z : |z| \leq 1\}$, but still they do not settle down near a *unique* finite limit. In fact, it is often tricky to prove from the definition that a given sequence is divergent. Instead we shall obtain two criteria which can be used to prove the divergence of such sequences. First, however, we need to discuss sequences which *tend to infinity*.

Definition The sequence $\{z_n\}$ **tends to infinity** if

for each positive number M, there is an integer N such that

$$|z_n| > M, \qquad \text{for all } n > N.$$

In this case we write

$$z_n \to \infty \text{ as } n \to \infty.$$

We do not write
$$\lim_{n \to \infty} z_n = \infty,$$
since this might suggest that ∞ is a complex number.

The geometric interpretation of this definition is that, no matter how large a circle we consider, the terms z_n eventually lie *outside* this circle. (Figure 1.11).

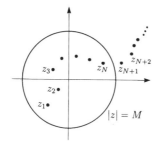

Figure 1.11 z_n eventually lies outside the circle $|z| = M$

For example, the sequence $\{2n + i\}$ tends to infinity because for each positive number M, there is an integer N such that

$$|2n + i| > M, \qquad \text{for all } n > N.$$

In this case, we can take $N = [M]$, for example, because

$$|2n + i| = \sqrt{4n^2 + 1} > 2n > n > M, \qquad \text{for all } n > [M].$$

The following result enables us to use our knowledge of null sequences to identify sequences which tend to infinity.

Theorem 1.5 Reciprocal Rule

Let $\{z_n\}$ be a sequence. Then

$$z_n \to \infty \text{ as } n \to \infty$$

if and only if

$$\{1/z_n\} \text{ is a null sequence.}$$

If $z_n \to \infty$ as $n \to \infty$, then only a finite number of terms of $\{z_n\}$ may be zero. In such a case, these terms are omitted from $\{z_n\}$ before forming $\{1/z_n\}$.

Proof We prove only the more important implication, that if $\{1/z_n\}$ is a null sequence, then $z_n \to \infty$ as $n \to \infty$.

We want to show that

for each positive number M, there is an integer N such that

$$|z_n| > M, \qquad \text{for all } n > N. \tag{$*$}$$

But the sequence $\{1/z_n\}$ is null and so we can choose an integer N such that

$$\left| \frac{1}{z_n} \right| < \frac{1}{M}, \qquad \text{for all } n > N.$$

This statement is equivalent to $(*)$, and so $z_n \to \infty$ as $n \to \infty$. ∎

The proof that '$z_n \to \infty$ as $n \to \infty \implies \{1/z_n\}$ is null' is similar.

Take $\varepsilon = 1/M$ in the definition of null sequence.

Remarks

1 The Reciprocal Rule does *not* assert that if $\{z_n\}$ is null, then $1/z_n \to \infty$ as $n \to \infty$. This statement is false; for example, the sequence $z_n = 0$, $n = 1, 2, \ldots$, is null but $1/z_n$, $n = 1, 2, \ldots$, is not defined and the sequence $\{1/z_n\}$ does not exist.

2 For sequences with real terms, there is a distinction between tending to $+\infty$ and tending to $-\infty$ (Figure 1.12). No such distinction is possible with complex sequences, and so there is a sense in which 'infinity' is a simpler place in complex analysis than in real analysis!

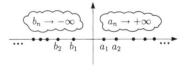

Figure 1.12

Example 1.3

Use the Reciprocal Rule to prove that the following sequences tend to infinity.

(a) $\{in^2/2\}$ (b) $\{(3i)^n - 2^n\}$

Solution

(a) Let $z_n = in^2/2$, for $n = 1, 2, \ldots$. Then

$$\frac{1}{z_n} = \frac{2}{in^2} = \left(\frac{2}{i} \right) \frac{1}{n^2}, \qquad \text{for } n = 1, 2, \ldots.$$

Since $\{1/n^2\}$ is a basic null sequence, we deduce that the sequence $\{1/z_n\}$ is null by the Multiple Rule. Hence the sequence $\{in^2/2\}$ tends to infinity, by the Reciprocal Rule.

(b) Let $z_n = (3i)^n - 2^n$, for $n = 1, 2, \ldots$. Then

$$\frac{1}{z_n} = \frac{1}{(3i)^n - 2^n} = \frac{(1/(3i))^n}{1 - (2/(3i))^n}.$$

$(3i)^n$ is the 'dominant term'.

Now $|1/(3i)| = 1/3 < 1$ and $|2/(3i)| = 2/3 < 1$, so that $\{(1/(3i))^n\}$ and $\{(2/(3i))^n\}$ are basic null sequences. Hence, by the Combination Rules,

$$\lim_{n \to \infty} \left(\frac{1}{z_n} \right) = \frac{0}{1 - 0} = 0,$$

so that the sequence $\{(3i)^n - 2^n\}$ tends to infinity, by the Reciprocal Rule. ∎

Problem 1.6

Use the Reciprocal Rule to prove that the sequence $\{n^3 - in^2 + (1+i)n\}$ tends to infinity.

Our two criteria for divergence both involve the idea of a *subsequence*. For example, consider the sequence $z_n = (-1)^n$, $n = 1, 2, \ldots$. This splits naturally into two:

> the even terms $z_2, z_4, z_6, \ldots, z_{2k}, \ldots$, each of which equals 1;
>
> the odd terms $z_1, z_3, z_5, \ldots, z_{2k-1}, \ldots$, each of which equals -1.

Both of these are sequences in their own right, and we call them the **even subsequence** $\{z_{2k}\}$ and the **odd subsequence** $\{z_{2k-1}\}$.

The first term in each case is given by $k = 1$.

In general, for a given sequence $\{z_n\}$ we may consider many different subsequences, such as

> $\{z_{3k}\}$, comprising the terms $z_3, z_6, z_9, \ldots$;
>
> $\{z_{4k+1}\}$, comprising the terms $z_5, z_9, z_{13}, \ldots$;
>
> $\{z_{k!}\}$, comprising the terms $z_1, z_2, z_6, \ldots$.

Definition   Let $\{n_k\}$ be a sequence of positive integers which is strictly increasing; that is,

$$n_1 < n_2 < n_3 < \ldots .$$

Then the sequence $\{z_{n_k}\}$ is a **subsequence** of the sequence $\{z_n\}$.

Note that any such sequence $\{n_k\}$ must satisfy
$$n_k \geq k, \quad \text{for } k = 1, 2, \ldots .$$

In the three examples above, $n_k = 3k$, $n_k = 4k + 1$, $n_k = k!$, respectively. In particular, if $z_n = i/(n+1)$, then $\{z_{k!}\}$ is given by

$$z_{k!} = i/(k! + 1), \qquad k = 1, 2, \ldots .$$

Problem 1.7

Let $z_n = in/(n+1)$, $n = 1, 2, \ldots$. Write down the first four terms of each of the subsequences $\{z_{n_k}\}$, where

(a) $n_k = 2k$;   (b) $n_k = 4k - 1$;   (c) $n_k = k^2$.

Now we can state our two criteria for establishing that a sequence is divergent.

Theorem 1.6   Subsequence Rules

(a) **First Subsequence Rule**   The sequence $\{z_n\}$ is divergent if $\{z_n\}$ has two convergent subsequences with different limits.

(b) **Second Subsequence Rule**   The sequence $\{z_n\}$ is divergent if $\{z_n\}$ has a subsequence which tends to infinity.

The proof of Theorem 1.6 is given in Subsection 1.3.

To see whether one of the Subsequence Rules can be applied to a given sequence, it is a good idea to write down the first few terms. For example,

> $\{(-1)^n i\}$ has terms $-i, i, -i, i, -i, i, \ldots$;
>
> $\{n^{(-1)^n}\}$ has terms $1, 2, \frac{1}{3}, 4, \frac{1}{5}, 6, \ldots$.

The even subsequence of $\{(-1)^n i\}$ has limit i, whereas the odd subsequence has limit $-i$, so $\{(-1)^n i\}$ is divergent by the First Subsequence Rule. However, the even subsequence of $\{n^{(-1)^n}\}$ tends to infinity, so $\{n^{(-1)^n}\}$ is divergent by the Second Subsequence Rule.

$2k^{(-1)^{2k}} = 2k$, for $k = 1, 2, \ldots .$

Problem 1.8

Use the Subsequence Rules to prove that each of the following sequences is divergent.

(a) $\{i^n\}$ (b) $\left\{n^2 \sin\left(\frac{1}{3}n\pi\right)\right\}$

In Theorem 1.2(b) you saw that the sequence $\{\alpha^n\}$ is null if $|\alpha| < 1$ and it is clear that $\{\alpha^n\}$ is convergent if $\alpha = 1$. We end this subsection by proving that $\{\alpha^n\}$ is divergent for all other values of α.

Theorem 1.7

(a) If $|\alpha| > 1$, then the sequence $\{\alpha^n\}$ tends to infinity.

(b) If $|\alpha| = 1$ and $\alpha \neq 1$, then the sequence $\{\alpha^n\}$ is divergent.

For example, $\{i^n\}$ is divergent.

These statements are depicted in Figures 1.13 and 1.14.

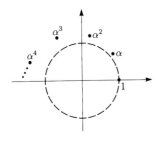

Figure 1.13 $|\alpha| > 1$ *Figure 1.14* $|\alpha| = 1,\ \alpha \neq 1$

Proof

(a) If $|\alpha| > 1$, then $\{(1/\alpha)^n\}$ is a basic null sequence (since $|1/\alpha| < 1$), and so the sequence $\{\alpha^n\}$ tends to infinity by the Reciprocal Rule.

(b) We use proof by contradiction. Assume that the sequence $\{\alpha^n\}$, where $|\alpha| = 1$ and $\alpha \neq 1$, converges to $\beta \in \mathbb{C}$, say. Then

$$|\beta| = \lim_{n \to \infty} |\alpha|^n = 1, \text{ by Theorem 1.4(a).}$$

Furthermore

$$\lim_{n \to \infty} \alpha^{n+1} = \alpha \lim_{n \to \infty} \alpha^n = \alpha\beta \quad \text{(Multiple Rule)}$$

and

$$\lim_{n \to \infty} \alpha^{n+1} = \beta,$$

since the sequence $\{\alpha^{n+1}\}$ is identical to the sequence $\{\alpha^n\}$, except that the first term is missing. Hence

$$\alpha\beta = \beta$$

and so $\beta = 0$, since $\alpha \neq 1$ (by hypothesis). This is a contradiction since $|\beta| = 1$, as shown above. Thus, we reject the assumption and conclude that $\{\alpha^n\}$ is divergent. ∎

1.3 Proofs

This subsection may be omitted on a first reading.

Here we give the proofs of the Basic Null Sequences, the Combination Rules and the Subsequence Rules.

Theorem 1.2 Basic Null Sequences

The following sequences are null.

(a) $\left\{ \dfrac{1}{n^p} \right\}$,   for $p > 0$.

(b) $\{\alpha^n\}$,   for $|\alpha| < 1$.

Proof

(a) We want to show that

for each positive number ε, there is an integer N such that

$$\frac{1}{n^p} < \varepsilon, \qquad \text{for all } n > N. \tag{$*$}$$

But, since $p > 0$,

$$\frac{1}{n^p} < \varepsilon \quad \Longleftrightarrow \quad n^p > \frac{1}{\varepsilon} \quad \Longleftrightarrow \quad n > (1/\varepsilon)^{1/p}.$$

Hence the statement $(*)$ holds if we take $N = [(1/\varepsilon)^{1/p}]$. Thus $\{1/n^p\}$ is a null sequence.

(b) If $\alpha = 0$, then the result is evident. If $0 < |\alpha| < 1$, then $|\alpha|$ can be written in the form

$$|\alpha| = \frac{1}{1+a}, \qquad \text{where } a > 0.$$

In fact,

$$a = \frac{1}{|\alpha|} - 1.$$

Now, by the Binomial Theorem,

$$(1+a)^n = 1 + na + \frac{n(n-1)}{2!}a^2 + \cdots + a^n, \qquad \text{for } n = 1, 2 \ldots,$$
$$\geq na$$

since $a > 0$. Hence

$$|\alpha|^n = \frac{1}{(1+a)^n} \leq \frac{1}{na} = \frac{(1/a)}{n}, \qquad \text{for } n = 1, 2, \ldots .$$

Now $\{(1/a)/n\}$ is a null sequence, by the Multiple Rule (proved next), and hence $\{\alpha^n\}$ is a null sequence, by the Squeeze Rule. ■

$\{1/n\}$ is a null sequence by part(a), with $p = 1$.

Theorem 1.3 Combination Rules

If $\displaystyle\lim_{n \to \infty} z_n = \alpha$ and $\displaystyle\lim_{n \to \infty} w_n = \beta$, then

Sum Rule $\qquad \displaystyle\lim_{n \to \infty} (z_n + w_n) = \alpha + \beta;$

Multiple Rule $\quad \displaystyle\lim_{n \to \infty} (\lambda z_n) = \lambda\alpha, \quad$ where $\lambda \in \mathbb{C};$

Product Rule $\quad \displaystyle\lim_{n \to \infty} (z_n w_n) = \alpha\beta;$

Quotient Rule $\quad \displaystyle\lim_{n \to \infty} \left(\frac{z_n}{w_n} \right) = \frac{\alpha}{\beta}, \quad$ provided that $\beta \neq 0.$

Proof

Sum Rule   We want to show that

for each positive number ε, there is an integer N such that

$$|(z_n + w_n) - (\alpha + \beta)| < \varepsilon, \qquad \text{for all } n > N. \tag{$*$}$$

Now

$$|(z_n + w_n) - (\alpha + \beta)| = |(z_n - \alpha) + (w_n - \beta)|$$
$$\leq |z_n - \alpha| + |w_n - \beta| \qquad \text{(Triangle Inequality).}$$

Since $\lim_{n \to \infty} z_n = \alpha$ and $\lim_{n \to \infty} w_n = \beta$, we know that there are integers N_1, N_2 such that

$$|z_n - \alpha| < \tfrac{1}{2}\varepsilon, \qquad \text{for all } n > N_1,$$
$$|w_n - \beta| < \tfrac{1}{2}\varepsilon, \qquad \text{for all } n > N_2.$$

> We use $\tfrac{1}{2}\varepsilon$ here, in order to obtain ε in $(*)$.

Hence, if $N = \max\{N_1, N_2\}$, then, for all $n > N$,

$$|(z_n + w_n) - (\alpha + \beta)| < \tfrac{1}{2}\varepsilon + \tfrac{1}{2}\varepsilon = \varepsilon,$$

as required.

Multiple Rule   We want to show that

for each positive number ε, there is an integer N such that

$$|\lambda z_n - \lambda \alpha| < \varepsilon, \qquad \text{for all } n > N. \tag{$*$}$$

If $\lambda = 0$, then this inequality is evident, so we assume that $\lambda \neq 0$. Since $\lim_{n \to \infty} z_n = \alpha$, we know that there is an integer N such that

$$|z_n - \alpha| < \frac{\varepsilon}{|\lambda|}, \qquad \text{for all } n > N.$$

> We use $\varepsilon/|\lambda|$ here in order to obtain ε in $(*)$.

Hence

$$|\lambda z_n - \lambda \alpha| = |\lambda||z_n - \alpha| < \varepsilon, \qquad \text{for all } n > N,$$

as required.

To prove the Product Rule we use the following lemma, which is also needed to prove the Second Subsequence Rule.

Lemma 1.1   If $\{z_n\}$ is a convergent sequence, then there is a positive number M such that

$$|z_n| \leq M, \qquad \text{for } n = 1, 2, \ldots. \tag{$*$}$$

> 'Every convergent sequence is bounded.'

Proof   Suppose that $\lim_{n \to \infty} z_n = \alpha$. Then there is an integer N such that

$$|z_n - \alpha| < 1, \qquad \text{for all } n > N.$$

> Take $\varepsilon = 1$ in the definition of convergence.

Now, by the Triangle Inequality,

$$|z_n| = |(z_n - \alpha) + \alpha| \leq |z_n - \alpha| + |\alpha|,$$

so that

$$|z_n| < 1 + |\alpha|, \qquad \text{for all } n > N.$$

Thus if $M = \max\{|z_1|, |z_2|, \ldots, |z_N|, 1 + |\alpha|\}$, then

$$|z_n| \leq M, \qquad \text{for } n = 1, 2, \ldots. \quad \blacksquare$$

Remark   If a sequence $\{z_n\}$ satisfies the property $(*)$ for a positive number M, then all the terms of the sequence lie in a closed disc with centre 0 and radius M. In this case, we say that the sequence is **bounded**.

We next prove the Product Rule.

Product Rule The idea here is to express the difference $z_n w_n - \alpha\beta$ in terms of $z_n - \alpha$ and $w_n - \beta$, as follows

$$z_n w_n - \alpha\beta = z_n(w_n - \beta) + \beta(z_n - \alpha).$$

By the Multiple Rule,

$$\lim_{n\to\infty} \beta(z_n - \alpha) = 0,$$

and, by Lemma 1.1, there is a positive number M such that

$$|z_n| \leq M, \qquad \text{for } n = 1, 2, \ldots.$$

Hence

$$|z_n(w_n - \beta)| = |z_n||w_n - \beta|,$$
$$\leq M|w_n - \beta|, \qquad \text{for } n = 1, 2, \ldots,$$

and so, by the Squeeze Rule and the Multiple Rule,

$$\lim_{n\to\infty} z_n(w_n - \beta) = 0.$$

Thus, by the Sum Rule,

$$\lim_{n\to\infty}(z_n w_n - \alpha\beta) = \lim_{n\to\infty} z_n(w_n - \beta) + \lim_{n\to\infty} \beta(z_n - \alpha)$$
$$= 0 + 0 = 0,$$

as required.

Quotient Rule Once again, we write the required difference in terms of $z_n - \alpha$ and $w_n - \beta$, as follows

$$\frac{z_n}{w_n} - \frac{\alpha}{\beta} = \frac{\beta(z_n - \alpha) - \alpha(w_n - \beta)}{w_n\beta}.$$

We know that the numerator sequence $\{\beta(z_n - \alpha) - \alpha(w_n - \beta)\}$ is null by the Sum and Multiple Rules, but there is a problem with the denominator. Some of the terms w_n may be 0, in which case z_n/w_n is undefined. However, we shall show that eventually $|w_n|$ is positive; in fact, we shall show that there is an integer N such that

$$\left|w_n\right| > \tfrac{1}{2}\left|\beta\right|, \qquad \text{for all } n > N \qquad (*)$$

(see Figure 1.15).

To prove $(*)$ we choose an integer N such that

$$\left|w_n - \beta\right| < \tfrac{1}{2}\left|\beta\right|, \qquad \text{for all } n > N,$$

so that, by the backwards form of the Triangle Inequality,

$$\left|w_n - \beta\right| < \tfrac{1}{2}\left|\beta\right| \implies |\beta| - |w_n| \leq \left|\beta - w_n\right| < \tfrac{1}{2}\left|\beta\right|$$
$$\implies |w_n| > |\beta| - \tfrac{1}{2}\left|\beta\right| = \tfrac{1}{2}\left|\beta\right|.$$

Thus, for all $n > N$,

$$\left|\frac{z_n}{w_n} - \frac{\alpha}{\beta}\right| = \frac{|\beta(z_n - \alpha) - \alpha(w_n - \beta)|}{|w_n||\beta|}$$
$$< \frac{2}{|\beta|^2}|\beta(z_n - \alpha) - \alpha(w_n - \beta)| \qquad \text{(by $(*)$)}.$$

Since the right-hand side defines a real null sequence of non-negative terms, we deduce that $\left\{\dfrac{z_n}{w_n} - \dfrac{\alpha}{\beta}\right\}$ is null, by the Squeeze Rule. ∎

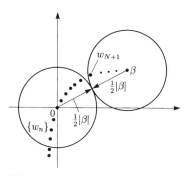

Figure 1.15 Eventually $|w_n| > \tfrac{1}{2}|\beta|$.

Take $\varepsilon = \tfrac{1}{2}|\beta|$ in the definition of convergence.

Theorem 1.6 Subsequence Rules

(a) **First Subsequence Rule** The sequence $\{z_n\}$ is divergent if $\{z_n\}$ has two convergent subsequences with different limits.

(b) **Second Subsequence Rule** The sequence $\{z_n\}$ is divergent if $\{z_n\}$ has a subsequence which tends to infinity.

Proof

(a) Since a given sequence is either convergent or divergent, it is sufficient to prove that if $\{z_n\}$ is convergent with limit α, then each subsequence $\{z_{n_k}\}$ is also convergent with limit α. We want to show that

for each positive number ε, there is an integer K such that

$$|z_{n_k} - \alpha| < \varepsilon, \qquad \text{for all } k > K.$$

Since $\lim_{n \to \infty} z_n = \alpha$, we know that there is an integer N such that

$$|z_n - \alpha| < \varepsilon, \qquad \text{for all } n > N.$$

Thus, if we take $K = N$, then

$$n_K \geq N,$$

so that

$$n_k > n_K \geq N, \qquad \text{for all } k > K,$$

and hence

$$|z_{n_k} - \alpha| < \varepsilon, \qquad \text{for all } k > K.$$

(b) If $\{z_n\}$ has a subsequence which tends to infinity, then $\{z_n\}$ cannot be bounded. Hence $\{z_n\}$ cannot be convergent, by Lemma 1.1. ■

2 CONTINUOUS FUNCTIONS

After working through this section, you should be able to:

(a) explain the statements 'the function f is continuous at the point α' and 'the function f is discontinuous at the point α';

(b) show that a function is *continuous/discontinuous* at a point by working from the definitions;

(c) use the Combination Rules, the Composition Rule and the Restriction Rule for continuous functions;

(d) recognize certain *basic continuous functions*;

(e) use the continuity of functions to evaluate the limits of certain sequences.

2.1 What is continuity? (audio-tape)

In real analysis the notion of a continuous function is introduced; such functions do not have jumps in their graphs (Figure 2.1). Roughly speaking, we say that the real function f is continuous at a point a provided that

  if x tends to a, then $f(x)$ tends to $f(a)$.

In this course, we shall take for granted that the following real functions are continuous at each point of their domains

  polynomial functions, rational functions, trigonometric and exponential functions and their inverses.

The continuity of a function f at a point α is important also in complex analysis and, by analogy, it can be described roughly as follows

  if z tends to α, then $f(z)$ tends to $f(\alpha)$.

In the audio tape we make this rough idea precise, using an approach based on the convergence of sequences.

Because we deal with so many convergent sequences, we shall often write simply '$z_n \to \alpha$', omitting the 'as $n \to \infty$'. Later in the audio tape we introduce an equivalent definition of continuity, the so-called ε-δ definition.

Before starting the tape, try the following problems. Their solutions are discussed in the frames, starting with Problem 2.1 in Frame 1.

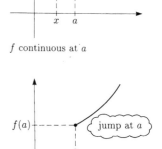

f continuous at a

f not continuous at a

Figure 2.1

The Greek lower case letter δ (delta) is commonly used to denote a small positive number.

Problem 2.1

Let $\{z_n\}$ be a sequence such that $\lim\limits_{n \to \infty} z_n = i$. Determine

  $\lim\limits_{n \to \infty} (z_n^2 + 3z_n)$.

Problem 2.2

Let $z_n = e^{i(\pi + 1/n)}, n = 1, 2, \dots$. Determine

  $\lim\limits_{n \to \infty} z_n$ and $\lim\limits_{n \to \infty} (\operatorname{Arg} z_n)$.

Also, write down $\operatorname{Arg}(-1)$.

(*Hint*: Plotting a few terms of $\{z_n\}$ should help you.)

NOW START THE TAPE.

3. Strategy for using definition

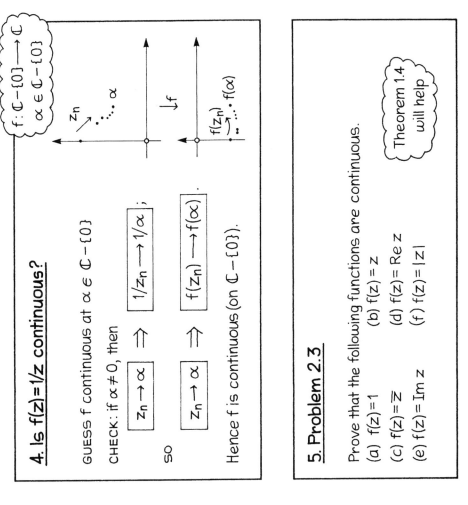

(cloud) $f: A \longrightarrow \mathbb{C}$, $\alpha \in A$

GUESS behaviour   CHECK definition

GUESS f continuous   CHECK definition HOLDS:

at α

$$\boxed{z_n \to \alpha} \implies \boxed{f(z_n) \to f(\alpha)}\,.$$

4. Is f(z)=1/z continuous?

(cloud) $f: \mathbb{C} - \{0\} \longrightarrow \mathbb{C}$, $\alpha \in \mathbb{C} - \{0\}$

GUESS f continuous at $\alpha \in \mathbb{C} - \{0\}$

CHECK: if $\alpha \neq 0$, then $\boxed{1/z_n \longrightarrow 1/\alpha}$;

so

$$\boxed{z_n \to \alpha} \implies \boxed{f(z_n) \longrightarrow f(\alpha)}\,.$$

Hence f is continuous (on $\mathbb{C} - \{0\}$).

5. Problem 2.3

Prove that the following functions are continuous.

(a) $f(z) = 1$ (b) $f(z) = z$

(c) $f(z) = \bar{z}$ (d) $f(z) = \operatorname{Re} z$

(e) $f(z) = \operatorname{Im} z$ (f) $f(z) = |z|$

(cloud) Theorem 1.4 will help

1. Reformulation of Problem 2.1

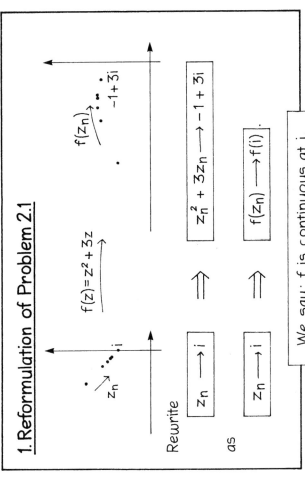

$f(z) = z^2 + 3z$

Rewrite

$$\boxed{z_n \to i} \implies \boxed{z_n^2 + 3z_n \longrightarrow -1 + 3i}$$

as

$$\boxed{z_n \to i} \implies \boxed{f(z_n) \longrightarrow f(i)}\,.$$

We say: f is continuous at i.

2. Continuity: sequential definition

(cloud) $f: A \longrightarrow \mathbb{C}$, $\alpha \in A$; e.g. $A = \mathbb{C}$, $A = \mathbb{C} - \{0\}$, or $A = \mathbb{R}$.

- **f is continuous at α** if for each sequence $\{z_n\}$ in A such that $z_n \to \alpha$, we have $f(z_n) \to f(\alpha)$;

that is,

$$\boxed{z_n \longrightarrow \alpha} \implies \boxed{f(z_n) \longrightarrow f(\alpha)}\,.$$

- **f is continuous** (on A) means that f is continuous at each α in A.

9. Is $r(z) = (1-3iz)/(z^2+4)$ continuous?

Combination Rules

If f and g are continuous at α, then so are:

- the **sum** $f + g$;
- the **multiple** λf, for $\lambda \in \mathbb{C}$;
- the **product** fg;
- the **quotient** f/g, provided that $g(\alpha) \neq 0$.

Hence $r(z) = (1-3iz)/(z^2+4)$
is continuous on $\mathbb{C} - \{-2i, 2i\}$.

10. Polynomial and rational functions

The following functions are continuous:

- any polynomial function
$p(z) = a_0 + a_1 z + \ldots + a_n z^n$
where $a_0, a_1, \ldots, a_n \in \mathbb{C}$;

- any rational function
$r(z) = p(z) / q(z)$.

Use Combination Rules: build up from $f(z)=1$, $f(z)=z$.

Domain of r excludes the zeros of q.

6. Reformulation of Problem 2.2

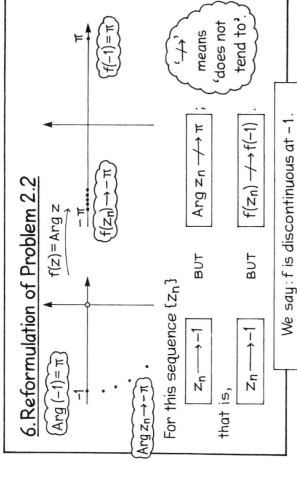

$\mathrm{Arg}(-1) = \pi$

$f(z) = \mathrm{Arg}\ z$

$\mathrm{Arg}\ z_n \to -\pi$

$f(z_n) \to -\pi$

$f(-1) = \pi$

For this sequence $\{z_n\}$

$z_n \to -1$ BUT $\boxed{\mathrm{Arg}\ z_n \not\to \pi}$;

$z_n \to -1$ BUT $\boxed{f(z_n) \not\to f(-1)}$.

that is,

We say: f is discontinuous at -1.

'$\not\to$' means 'does not tend to'.

7. Discontinuous functions

- f is **discontinuous at** α if f is not continuous at α.

$f: A \to \mathbb{C}$
$\alpha \in A$

STRATEGY:

GUESS f discontinuous at α

CHECK definition FAILS:

Find ONE $\{z_n\}$ in A such that

$\boxed{z_n \to \alpha}$ BUT $\boxed{f(z_n) \not\to f(\alpha)}$.

8. Problem 2.4

Prove that $f(z) = \mathrm{Arg}\ z$
is discontinuous at all $\alpha \in \mathbb{R}$, with $\alpha < 0$.

11. Is $h(z) = |z^2+1|$ continuous?

Composition Rule

If f is continuous at α and g is continuous at $f(\alpha)$, then $g \circ f$ is continuous at α.

TAKE: $f(z) = z^2+1$, $g(z) = |z|$.

(f and g are both continuous.)

Hence $h(z) = |z^2+1|$ is continuous (on $\mathbb{C}$).

h is a composite function; $h = g \circ f$, $h(z) = g(f(z))$.

$$g(f(z)) = |z^2+1|$$

---

12. Is $f(z) = e^z$ continuous?

$$f(z) = e^{x+iy} = e^x(\cos y + i \sin y)$$
$$= e^{Re\,z}(\cos(Im\,z) + i \sin(Im\,z))$$

Now the following functions are continuous:

- $z \longmapsto Re\,z$ and $z \longmapsto Im\,z$;
- *real* trigonometric and exponential functions.

Hence $f(z) = e^z$ is continuous on $\mathbb{C}$.

Combination of composite functions

Composition and Combination Rules

Also continuous:
complex trigonometric and hyperbolic functions.
(sin, cos, tan)   (sinh, cosh, tanh)

e.g. $f(z) = \sin z$
$$= \frac{e^{iz} - e^{-iz}}{2i}$$

---

13. Is $f(x) = x + ix^2$ $(x \in \mathbb{R})$ continuous?

Restriction Rule

If f has domain A, g has domain B and

1. f is the restriction of g to A,
2. g is continuous at $\alpha \in A$,

then f is continuous at α.

TAKE: $g(z) = z + iz^2$, $B = \mathbb{C}$, $A = \mathbb{R}$; then g is continuous and $f(x) = g(x)$, for $x \in \mathbb{R}$.

Hence $f(x) = x + ix^2$ $(x \in \mathbb{R})$ is continuous.

APPLICATION: to parametrized paths.

$\gamma(t) = t + it^2$ $(t \in \mathbb{R})$ is continuous.

f is the restriction of $g(z) = z + iz^2$ to $\mathbb{R}$.

---

14. Problem 2.5

Use the above rules to determine whether the following functions are continuous.

(a) $f(z) = e^{-z^2}$

(b) $f(x) = \dfrac{x^2 + i}{x^2 - i}$ $(x \in \mathbb{R})$

(c) $f(z) = \log_e |z|$

(d) $f(z) = Re(z^2+1) - |z|^2$

17. Where is $f(z) = \text{Arg } z$ continuous?

Discontinuous at all points of $\{x \in \mathbb{R} : x < 0\}$: Frame 8.

Let $A = \mathbb{C} - \{x \in \mathbb{R} : x \leq 0\}$ and $\alpha \in A$.

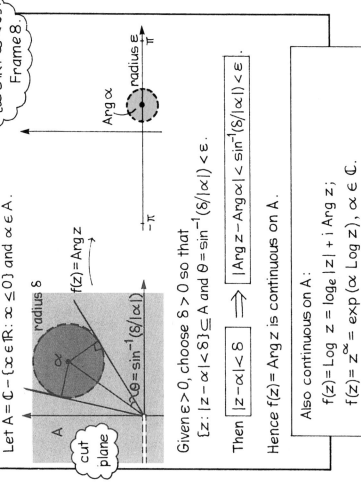

Given $\varepsilon > 0$, choose $\delta > 0$ so that
$$\{z : |z - \alpha| < \delta\} \subseteq A \text{ and } \theta = \sin^{-1}(\delta/|\alpha|) < \varepsilon.$$

Then $|z - \alpha| < \delta \implies |\text{Arg } z - \text{Arg } \alpha| < \sin^{-1}(\delta/|\alpha|) < \varepsilon.$

Hence $f(z) = \text{Arg } z$ is continuous on A.

Also continuous on A:
$$f(z) = \text{Log } z = \log_e |z| + i \text{ Arg } z;$$
$$f(z) = z^\alpha = \exp(\alpha \text{ Log } z), \ \alpha \in \mathbb{C}.$$

18. Basic continuous functions

- polynomial and rational functions;
- $f(z) = |z|, \ \bar{z}, \ \text{Re } z, \ \text{Im } z;$
- $f(z) = e^z;$
- trigonometric and hyperbolic functions;
- $f(z) = \text{Arg } z, \ \text{Log } z, \ z^\alpha, \quad$ on $\mathbb{C} - \{x \in \mathbb{R} : x \leq 0\}.$

15. Motivating the ε-δ definition: $f(z) = 2iz$

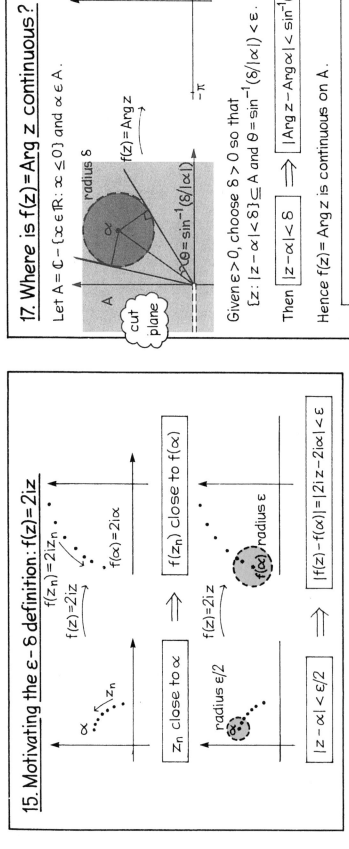

$f(z_n) = 2iz_n$

$f(z) = 2iz$

$f(\alpha) = 2i\alpha$

z_n close to α $\implies$ $f(z_n)$ close to $f(\alpha)$

$f(z) = 2iz$

radius ε

$|z - \alpha| < \varepsilon/2 \implies |f(z) - f(\alpha)| = |2iz - 2i\alpha| < \varepsilon$

radius $\varepsilon/2$

16. Continuity: ε-δ definition

- f is continuous at α if

for each $\varepsilon > 0$, there is $\delta > 0$ such that

$z \in A, |z - \alpha| < \delta \implies |f(z) - f(\alpha)| < \varepsilon.$

$f: A \longrightarrow \mathbb{C}$
$\alpha \in A$

radius ε

radius δ

In the audio tape we introduced several techniques for proving that a given function f is continuous at a point α in its domain:

1. use the sequential definition in Frame 2;
2. use the Combination Rules, Composition Rule or Restriction Rule together with the list of basic continuous functions in Frame 18;
3. use the ε-δ definition in Frame 16.

In most cases you will be able to verify that a given function f is continuous using the second technique — you should resort to the definitions only if you think that f is discontinuous at α, or you can find no other way to prove that f is continuous at α. (See Problem 2.8.)

Problem 2.6

Prove that the following function is continuous.

$$f(z) = \sin\left(\frac{z^2 + 1}{z - 2i}\right) \qquad (z \in A),$$

where $A = \{z : -1 \leq \operatorname{Re} z \leq 1, -1 \leq \operatorname{Im} z \leq 1\}$.

We can use the fact that a function f is continuous at a point α to evaluate limits of sequences of the form $\{f(z_n)\}$, where the sequence $\{z_n\}$ has limit α. For, it follows immediately from the definition of continuity that

if the function f is continuous at α and $\lim_{n \to \infty} z_n = \alpha$, then
$$\lim_{n \to \infty} f(z_n) = f(\alpha).$$

Example 2.1

Evaluate $\lim_{n \to \infty} \operatorname{Log}(1 + i/n)$.

Solution

The sequence

$$z_n = 1 + i/n, \qquad n = 1, 2, \ldots,$$

has limit 1 (Sum Rule), and 1 is a point at which the function $f(z) = \operatorname{Log} z$ is continuous (Frame 18). Hence (by the above result)

$$\lim_{n \to \infty} \operatorname{Log}(1 + i/n) = \operatorname{Log} 1 = 0. \quad \blacksquare$$

Problem 2.7

Evaluate each of the following limits (of sequences).

(a) $\lim_{n \to \infty} \sin(\pi - 2/n)$ (b) $\lim_{n \to \infty} \operatorname{Arg}(i + 1/n^2)$

(c) $\lim_{n \to \infty} \exp(-i\pi/2 + i/(2n))$

Continuity: a 'local' property

Continuity is a property of a function at a point; it is a 'local' property in the following sense. Whether or not a function f is continuous at a point α depends only on the values taken by f in an open disc with centre α (no matter how small the radius of the disc) in the domain of f. (This follows from the definition of continuity.)

As an application of this property, consider the two functions

$$f(z) = z^{1/2} \qquad (z \in \mathbb{C} - \{x \in \mathbb{R} : x \leq 0\})$$

and

$$g(z) = z^{1/2} \qquad (z \in \mathbb{C}),$$

which have the same rule, but different domains.

As you know from the audio tape, the function f is continuous at each point of its domain $\mathbb{C} - \{x \in \mathbb{R} : x \leq 0\}$, since

$$f(z) = \exp\left(\tfrac{1}{2}\operatorname{Log} z\right) \qquad (z \in \mathbb{C} - \{x \in \mathbb{R} : x \leq 0\}).$$

From this we deduce that the function g is also continuous at each point of $\mathbb{C} - \{x \in \mathbb{R} : x \leq 0\}$. For, if $\alpha \in \mathbb{C} - \{x \in \mathbb{R} : x \leq 0\}$, then g takes the same value as f at each point of some open disc with centre α, and the continuity of g at α then follows from that of f because continuity is a local property.

See Example 4.1(c) for one method of choosing such an open disc with centre α.

In the following problem, you are asked to investigate the continuity of g at the other points of its domain $\mathbb{C}$.

Problem 2.8

Show that the function

$$g(z) = z^{1/2} \qquad (z \in \mathbb{C})$$

is

(a) discontinuous at each point $\alpha \in \{x \in \mathbb{R} : x < 0\}$;

(b) continuous at 0, by using the ε-δ definition of continuity.

(*Hint for part (a)*: Consider the sequence $\{z_n\}$ of Problem 2.4 and use the result of Problem 2.7(c).)

2.2 Proofs

In this subsection we prove the Combination, Composition and Restriction Rules, and we also prove that the two definitions of continuity, given in Frames 2 and 16, are equivalent.

This subsection may be omitted on a first reading.

Theorem 2.1 Combination Rules

If the functions f and g are continuous at α, then so are the following functions:

Sum Rule	$f + g$;
Multiple Rule	λf, for $\lambda \in \mathbb{C}$;
Product Rule	fg;
Quotient Rule	f/g, provided that $g(\alpha) \neq 0$.

The proofs of these four rules are very similar to, and depend on, the corresponding results for sequences. We prove only the Sum Rule.

Proof

Sum Rule   We want to prove that

for each sequence $\{z_n\}$ in the domain of $f + g$ such that $z_n \to \alpha$,
$$f(z_n) + g(z_n) \to f(\alpha) + g(\alpha).$$

We know that $\{z_n\}$ lies in the domain of f and in the domain of g, and also that both f and g are continuous at α. Hence

$$f(z_n) \to f(\alpha) \qquad \text{and} \qquad g(z_n) \to g(\alpha),$$

and so, by the Sum Rule for sequences,

$$f(z_n) + g(z_n) \to f(\alpha) + g(\alpha),$$

as required.   ∎

26

Next, recall the Composition Rule.

Theorem 2.2 Composition Rule

If the function f is continuous at α, and if the function g is continuous at $f(\alpha)$, then $g \circ f$ is continuous at α.

Proof We want to prove that

for each sequence $\{z_n\}$ in the domain of $g \circ f$ such that $z_n \to \alpha$,

$$g(f(z_n)) \to g(f(\alpha)).$$

We know that $\{z_n\}$ lies in the domain of f, and that f is continuous at α. Hence

$$f(z_n) \to f(\alpha).$$

We also know that $\{f(z_n)\}$ lies in the domain of g, and that g is continuous at $f(\alpha)$. Hence

$$g(f(z_n)) \to g(f(\alpha)), \quad \text{as required.} \quad \blacksquare$$

The proof of our next result is particularly straightforward.

Theorem 2.3 Restriction Rule

If the function f has domain A, the function g has domain B and

1. f is the restriction of g to A,

2. g is continuous at $\alpha \in A$,

then f is continuous at α.

Thus $A \subseteq B$ and
$$f(z) = g(z), \quad \text{for } z \in A.$$

Proof We want to prove that

for each sequence $\{z_n\}$ in A such that $z_n \to \alpha$,

$$f(z_n) \to f(\alpha).$$

Since $\{z_n\}$ and α lie in B, $g(z_n) \to g(\alpha)$. Therefore, since

$$f(z_n) = g(z_n), \text{ for } n = 1, 2, \ldots, \quad \text{and} \quad f(\alpha) = g(\alpha),$$

we deduce that $f(z_n) \to f(\alpha)$, as required. $\quad \blacksquare$

Finally, we prove the equivalence of our two definitions of continuity.

Theorem 2.4 The ε-δ definition of continuity is equivalent to the sequential definition of continuity.

Proof A function f with domain A is either continuous or not at $\alpha \in A$, according to the ε-δ definition. We give the proof in two parts.

(a) Assume first that f does satisfy the ε-δ definition of continuity at $\alpha \in A$. We want to deduce that if $\{z_n\}$ is any sequence in A such that $z_n \to \alpha$, then $f(z_n) \to f(\alpha)$ (so that f satisfies the sequential definition of continuity at α).

Note the conventional use of 'any' in this sentence to cover the 'each' which appears in the definition of continuity.

Suppose, therefore, that $\varepsilon > 0$ is given. By our assumption, there is a positive δ such that

$$|f(z) - f(\alpha)| < \varepsilon, \qquad \text{for all } z \in A \text{ with } |z - \alpha| < \delta,$$

See Frame 16.

and then there is an integer N such that

$$|z_n - \alpha| < \delta, \qquad \text{for all } n > N.$$

Hence
$$|f(z_n) - f(\alpha)| < \varepsilon, \qquad \text{for all } n > N,$$
so that $f(z_n) \to f(\alpha)$, as required.

(b) Next assume that f does *not* satisfy the ε-δ definition of continuity at $\alpha \in A$. We want to find a sequence $\{z_n\}$ in A with $z_n \to \alpha$ but $f(z_n) \nrightarrow f(\alpha)$ (so that f does not satisfy the sequential definition of continuity at α).

By our assumption, there is some $\varepsilon > 0$ such that, for *each* $\delta > 0$,
$$|f(z) - f(\alpha)| \geq \varepsilon, \qquad \text{for some } z \in A \text{ with } |z - \alpha| < \delta.$$

The phrase 'for some $z \in A$ with $|z - \alpha| < \delta$' means that there is at least one such z and that we are interested in just one of them.

Applying this statement with $\delta = 1/n, n = 1, 2, \ldots$, we find that
$$|f(z_n) - f(\alpha)| \geq \varepsilon, \qquad \text{for some } z_n \in A \text{ with } |z_n - \alpha| < 1/n.$$

The numbers $z_n, n = 1, 2, \ldots$, form a sequence in A with $z_n \to \alpha$ but $f(z_n) \nrightarrow f(\alpha)$, as required. ∎

All the terms of the sequence $\{f(z_n)\}$ lie outside the circle with centre $f(\alpha)$ and radius ε.

3 LIMITS OF FUNCTIONS

After working through this section, you should be able to:

(a) show that a point α is a *limit point* of a set A;

(b) explain the statement 'the function f has limit β as z tends to α', and evaluate such limits by working from the definition;

(c) establish that certain functions do not have limits at specified points;

(d) understand the relationship between limits and continuity, and use it to evaluate certain limits of functions;

(e) use the Combination Rules to calculate limits of functions.

3.1 What is a limit of a function?

We begin by looking in detail at the rational function
$$f(z) = \frac{z^2 + 1}{z - i}.$$

The domain of this function is $\mathbb{C} - \{i\}$ because the denominator $z - i$ equals zero when $z = i$. However, the function f is actually rather well-behaved as z approaches this missing point i. To see why this is the case, notice that
$$f(z) = \frac{z^2 + 1}{z - i} = \frac{(z - i)(z + i)}{z - i} = z + i, \qquad \text{for } z \in \mathbb{C} - \{i\}.$$

The factor $z - i$ can be cancelled here because $z \in \mathbb{C} - \{i\}$. This equivalent formula for $f(z)$ makes it clear that, if z tends to i, then $f(z)$ tends to $i + i = 2i$.

The behaviour of this function f near i is an example of a function *tending to a limit* as z tends to a point α. In order to define this concept for a general function f, we need to ensure that f is defined *near* the point α, but not necessarily *at* the point α. To do this we introduce the idea of a *limit point* of a set A.

> **Definition** The point α is a **limit point** of a set A if there is a sequence $\{z_n\}$ in $A - \{\alpha\}$ such that
>
> $$\lim_{n \to \infty} z_n = \alpha.$$

Some texts use the name 'cluster point' or 'accumulation point' for this concept.

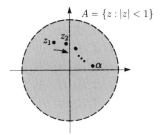

Figure 3.1

If α is a limit point of A, then it is possible to approach α along a sequence $\{z_n\}$ of points, each of which belongs to A but none of which is equal to α. As an example, consider the open disc

$$A = \{z : |z| < 1\}.$$

Figure 3.1 indicates that each point α of A is a limit point of A, but it is also true that each boundary point of A is a limit point of A. For example, consider $\alpha = i$; all points of the sequence

$$z_n = i - i/n, \qquad n = 1, 2, \ldots,$$

lie in A and are different from i (Figure 3.2), but $\lim_{n \to \infty} z_n = i$, so that i is a limit point of A.

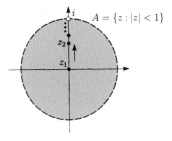

Figure 3.2

On the other hand, if $A = \mathbb{Z}$, then $\alpha = 1 \in \mathbb{Z}$, but α is not a limit point of A; in fact, A has no limit points in this case.

Problem 3.1

Prove that each of the following points α is a limit point of the corresponding set A.

(a) $\alpha = 0$, $A = \{z : |z| < 1\}$ (b) $\alpha = i$, $A = \{z : \operatorname{Re} z > 0\}$
(c) $\alpha = 1$, $A = \{z : |z| = 1\}$ (d) $\alpha = 2$, $A = \mathbb{C} - \{2\}$
(e) $\alpha = -1$, $A = \mathbb{R} - \{-1\}$

We now define the *limit of a function* using the convergence of sequences, in a manner reminiscent of the definition of continuity.

> **Definition** Let f be a function with domain A, and suppose that α is a limit point of A. Then the function f has **limit β as z tends to α** if
>
> for each sequence z_n in $A - \{\alpha\}$ such that $z_n \to \alpha$,
>
> $$f(z_n) \to \beta.$$
>
> In this case we write
>
> EITHER $\lim_{z \to \alpha} f(z) = \beta$,
>
> OR $f(z) \to \beta$ as $z \to \alpha$.

Note that the *limit point* α is associated with the set A, whereas the *limit* β is associated with the function f.

Figure 3.3 illustrates this definition.

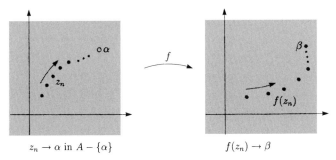

$z_n \to \alpha$ in $A - \{\alpha\}$ $f(z_n) \to \beta$

Figure 3.3

Remarks

1 Since the sequences considered here lie in $A - \{\alpha\}$, the value $f(\alpha)$ need not be defined in order for $\lim\limits_{z \to \alpha} f(z)$ to exist. Even when $f(\alpha)$ is defined, its value has no bearing on the existence or value of this limit.

2 The expression $\lim\limits_{z \to \alpha} f(z) = \beta$ contains no reference to any sequence — this signifies that the limit is independent of the route taken to α through $A - \{\alpha\}$.

Earlier you saw that the function $f(z) = (z^2 + 1)/(z - i)$ can be written in the form

$$f(z) = \frac{z^2 + 1}{z - i} = z + i \qquad (z \in \mathbb{C} - \{i\}).$$

Thus if $\{z_n\}$ is any sequence in $\mathbb{C} - \{i\}$ such that $z_n \to i$, then

$$f(z_n) = z_n + i \to i + i = 2i,$$

by the Sum Rule for sequences. Hence $\lim\limits_{z \to i} f(z) = 2i$, as expected.

Example 3.1

Prove that each of the following limits exists, and evaluate them.

(a) $\lim\limits_{z \to 2} \dfrac{z^2 - 4}{z - 2}$

(b) $\lim\limits_{x \to -1} \dfrac{x^3 + x^2 + ix + i}{x + 1}$

Solution

(a) First note that the domain of the function $f(z) = (z^2 - 4)/(z - 2)$ is $\mathbb{C} - \{2\}$ and that 2 is a limit point of this set (by Problem 3.1(d)).

Next, notice that

$$f(z) = \frac{z^2 - 4}{z - 2} = z + 2, \qquad \text{for } z \in \mathbb{C} - \{2\}.$$

Thus if $\{z_n\}$ is any sequence lying in $\mathbb{C} - \{2\}$ such that $z_n \to 2$, then

$$f(z_n) = z_n + 2 \to 4,$$

by the Sum Rule for sequences. Hence

$$\lim_{z \to 2} \frac{z^2 - 4}{z - 2} = 4.$$

(b) First note that the domain of $f(x) = (x^3 + x^2 + ix + i)/(x + 1)$ is $\mathbb{R} - \{-1\}$ and that -1 is a limit point of this set (by Problem 3.1(e)).

Remember that x is used to denote a real variable.

Next, notice that

$$\begin{aligned} f(x) &= \frac{x^3 + x^2 + ix + i}{x + 1} \\ &= \frac{(x + 1)(x^2 + i)}{x + 1} \\ &= x^2 + i, \qquad \text{for } x \in \mathbb{R} - \{-1\}. \end{aligned}$$

Thus if $\{x_n\}$ is any sequence lying in $\mathbb{R} - \{-1\}$ such that $x_n \to -1$, then

$$f(x_n) = x_n^2 + i \to (-1)^2 + i = 1 + i,$$

by the Combination Rules for sequences. Hence

$$\lim_{x \to -1} \frac{x^3 + x^2 + ix + i}{x + 1} = 1 + i. \qquad \blacksquare$$

Problem 3.2

Prove that the following limit exists, and evaluate it.

$$\lim_{z \to i} \frac{z^3 + i}{z - i}$$

Our next example illustrates how to prove that a limit does not exist, by showing that there is no β such that $f(z_n) \to \beta$ for *each* sequence $\{z_n\}$ which tends to α through $A - \{\alpha\}$.

Example 3.2

Prove that each of the following limits does not exist.

(a) $\lim\limits_{z \to 0} z/\bar{z}$ (b) $\lim\limits_{z \to 0} 1/z$

Solution

(a) The function $f(z) = z/\bar{z}$ has domain $\mathbb{C} - \{0\}$ and 0 is a limit point of this set. However,

if $z = x$, with $x \in \mathbb{R} - \{0\}$, then $f(z) = f(x) = x/x = 1$;

if $z = iy$, with $y \in \mathbb{R} - \{0\}$, then $f(z) = f(iy) = (iy)/(-iy) = -1$.

This shows that $f(z)$ behaves in different ways as z approaches 0 in different directions. To exploit this we choose simple sequences tending to 0 in the two directions.

Thus, if

$$z_n = \frac{1}{n}, \quad n = 1, 2, \ldots, \qquad \text{and} \qquad z_n' = \frac{i}{n}, \quad n = 1, 2, \ldots,$$

then both sequences $\{z_n\}$, $\{z_n'\}$ lie in the domain $\mathbb{C} - \{0\}$ and tend to 0, but

$$\lim_{n \to \infty} f(z_n) = 1, \quad \text{whereas} \quad \lim_{n \to \infty} f(z_n') = -1.$$

This is summarized in Figure 3.4.

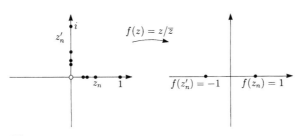

Figure 3.4

Hence there is no number β such that $f(z_n) \to \beta$ for each sequence $\{z_n\}$ which tends to 0 through $\mathbb{C} - \{0\}$, and so f does not tend to a limit as $z \to 0$.

(b) The domain of $f(z) = 1/z$ is $\mathbb{C} - \{0\}$ and 0 is a limit point of this set. However, the sequence $z_n = 1/n, n = 1, 2, \ldots$, lies in $\mathbb{C} - \{0\}$ and

$$f(z_n) = 1/z_n = n \to \infty \text{ as } n \to \infty.$$

Hence there is no number β such that $f(z_n) \to \beta$ for each sequence $\{z_n\}$ which tends to 0 through $\mathbb{C} - \{0\}$, and so f does not tend to a limit as z tends to 0. ∎

Remark   In fact, $1/z \to \infty$ as $z \to 0$. We discuss this type of behaviour later in the course.

We now summarize these techniques in the form of alternative strategies.

Strategy for proving the non-existence of limits

To prove that $\lim_{z \to \alpha} f(z)$ does not exist, where α is a limit point of the domain A of the function f:

EITHER

(a) find two sequences $\{z_n\}$ and $\{z_n'\}$ in $A - \{\alpha\}$ which both tend to α, such that the sequences $\{f(z_n)\}$ and $\{f(z_n')\}$ have different limits;

OR

(b) find a sequence $\{z_n\}$ in $A - \{\alpha\}$ which tends to α, such that the sequence $\{f(z_n)\}$ tends to infinity.

Note the similarity of this strategy to Theorem 1.6, the Subsequence Rules.

Problem 3.3

Prove that $\lim_{z \to 0}(z/\operatorname{Re} z)$ does not exist.

3.2 Limits and continuity

Comparison of the definition of *limit* given in this section with the definition of *continuity* given in the previous section shows that there is a close connection between these notions. The following result makes this connection precise.

Theorem 3.1 Let f be a function with domain A and suppose that the point $\alpha \in A$ is a limit point of A. Then

$$f \text{ is continuous at } \alpha \iff \lim_{z \to \alpha} f(z) = f(\alpha).$$

Before discussing the proof, we note that Theorem 3.1 allows many limits to be evaluated very easily. For example, to evaluate

$$\lim_{z \to i}(3z^4 - iz^3 + 1)$$

notice that the function $f(z) = 3z^4 - iz^3 + 1$ has domain $\mathbb{C}$ and is continuous at i (since f is a polynomial function) and that i is a limit point of $\mathbb{C}$. Hence, by Theorem 3.1,

$$\lim_{z \to i}(3z^4 - iz^3 + 1) = f(i) = 3.$$

Problem 3.4

Evaluate the following limits.

(a) $\lim_{z \to i} \exp(z^2 + 1)$ (b) $\lim_{x \to \pi} e^{ix}$

Proof of Theorem 3.1

Suppose first that f is continuous at α. If $\{z_n\}$ is any sequence in $A - \{\alpha\}$ with $z_n \to \alpha$, then it follows (because f is continuous at α) that $f(z_n) \to f(\alpha)$. Hence $\lim_{z \to \alpha} f(z) = f(\alpha)$, as required.

Suppose next that $\lim_{z \to \alpha} f(z) = f(\alpha)$. If $\{z_n\}$ is any sequence in A with $z_n \to \alpha$, and $\{z_{n_k}\}$ is the subsequence of terms of $\{z_n\}$ which differ from α, then

$$f(z_{n_k}) \to f(\alpha) \quad (\text{since } z_{n_k} \to \alpha \text{ and } \lim_{z \to \alpha} f(z) = f(\alpha)).$$

The remaining subsequence $\{z_{m_k}\}$ of $\{z_n\}$ is of the form

$$z_{m_k} = \alpha, \qquad k = 1, 2, \ldots;$$

so it is certainly true that

$$f(z_{m_k}) = f(\alpha) \to f(\alpha).$$

Thus $\{f(z_n)\}$ consists of two subsequences each of which converges to $f(\alpha)$, and so

$$f(z_n) \to f(\alpha);$$

hence f is continuous at α. ∎

See Exercise 1.6 for a proof of this assertion.

Remark Just as for continuity, the definition of limit can be reformulated in ε-δ terms, as follows.

Definition Let f be a function with domain A and suppose that α is a limit point of A. Then the function f **has limit β as z tends to α** if

for each positive ε, there is a positive δ such that
$$|f(z) - \beta| < \varepsilon, \qquad \text{for all } z \in A - \{\alpha\} \text{ with } |z - \alpha| < \delta.$$

The proof that this definition is equivalent to the earlier sequential definition is very similar to that of the corresponding result for continuity (Theorem 2.4).

3.3 Rules for limits

As you might expect (from your experience with limits of sequences and continuous functions), limits can often be evaluated by applying various rules, such as the following.

Theorem 3.2 Combination Rules

Let f and g be functions with domains A and B, respectively, and suppose that α is a limit point of $A \cap B$. If

$$\lim_{z \to \alpha} f(z) = \beta \qquad \text{and} \qquad \lim_{z \to \alpha} g(z) = \gamma,$$

then

Sum Rule $\lim_{z \to \alpha} (f(z) + g(z)) = \beta + \gamma$;

Multiple Rule $\lim_{z \to \alpha} (\lambda f(z)) = \lambda\beta, \qquad$ for $\lambda \in \mathbb{C}$;

Product Rule $\lim_{z \to \alpha} (f(z)g(z)) = \beta\gamma$;

Quotient Rule $\lim_{z \to \alpha} (f(z)/g(z)) = \beta/\gamma, \quad$ provided that $\gamma \neq 0$.

If α is a limit point of $A \cap B$, then clearly it is also a limit point of A and of B.

The proofs of these rules are straightforward and depend on the analogous results for sequences (see Theorem 1.3); we omit them.

Here is a simple application. Since

$$\lim_{z \to i} \frac{z^2 + 1}{z - i} = 2i \qquad \text{and} \qquad \lim_{z \to i}(z^3 + 1) = -i + 1,$$

we deduce that

$$\lim_{z \to i}\left(\frac{z^2 + 1}{z - i} + (z^3 + 1)\right) = 2i + (-i + 1) = 1 + i,$$

by the Sum Rule for limits.

The intersection of the domains of the functions $f(z) = (z^2 + 1)/(z - i)$ and $g(z) = z^3 + 1$ is $\mathbb{C} - \{i\}$, and i is a limit point of this set.

There is also a Composition Rule for limits, but its statement is much more complicated than the Composition Rule for continuous functions, and so we just give one example here of a 'composed limit'.

Example 3.3

Evaluate the following limit.

$$\lim_{z \to i} \sin\left(\frac{z^2 + 1}{z - i}\right)$$

Solution

Since we know that

$$\lim_{z \to i} \frac{z^2 + 1}{z - i} = 2i,$$

it seems likely that

$$\lim_{z \to i} \sin\left(\frac{z^2 + 1}{z - i}\right) = \sin(2i). \tag{3.1}$$

Note that i is not in the domain of the function

$$f(z) = \sin\left(\frac{z^2 + 1}{z - i}\right),$$

so Theorem 3.1 is not applicable here.

To establish this, we use the continuity of the sine function at the point $2i$.

If $\{z_n\}$ is any sequence in $\mathbb{C} - \{i\}$ such that $z_n \to i$, then the sequence
$\left\{\dfrac{z_n^2 + 1}{z_n - i}\right\}$ is such that

$$\frac{z_n^2 + 1}{z_n - i} = z_n + i \to 2i.$$

Hence the sequence $\left\{\sin\left(\dfrac{z_n^2 + 1}{z_n - i}\right)\right\}$ is such that

$$\sin\left(\frac{z_n^2 + 1}{z_n - i}\right) = \sin(z_n + i) \to \sin(2i),$$

since the sine function is continuous at the point $2i$. This proves that Equation (3.1) does hold. ∎

Problem 3.5

Evaluate the following limit.

$$\lim_{x \to 1} \exp\left(i\,\frac{x^2 - 1}{x - 1}\right)$$

4 REGIONS

After working through this section, you should be able to:

(a) determine whether or not a given subset of $\mathbb{C}$ is: *open, convex, connected*;

(b) explain the statement '$\mathcal{R}$ is a region of $\mathbb{C}$';

(c) recognize certain *basic regions*.

4.1 Domains of complex functions

Various sets occur as the domains of complex functions. For example,

the function $f(z) = \sin z$ has domain $\mathbb{C}$;

the function $f(z) = 1/z$ has domain $\mathbb{C} - \{0\}$;

the function $f(z) = \tan z$ has domain $\mathbb{C} - \left\{ \left(n + \frac{1}{2}\right) \pi : n \in \mathbb{Z} \right\}$.

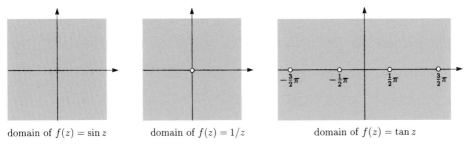

domain of $f(z) = \sin z$ domain of $f(z) = 1/z$ domain of $f(z) = \tan z$

Figure 4.1

Although these sets are all different, they have certain features in common. For example, each of the sets is 'unbounded'; that is, they do not lie inside any circle in $\mathbb{C}$.

A less obvious property of these sets is the following: each point in the set can be surrounded by an open disc lying entirely within the set. For example, the point 1 in $\mathbb{C} - \{0\}$ is the centre of the open disc $\left\{z : |z - 1| < \frac{1}{2}\right\}$ which lies entirely in $\mathbb{C} - \{0\}$ (Figure 4.2). Sets with this property are called *open*.

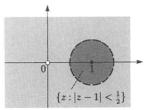

$\{z : |z - 1| < \frac{1}{2}\}$

Figure 4.2

Another property of these sets is the following: each pair of points in the set can be joined by a path lying entirely in the set. For example, as shown in Figure 4.3, the points 1 and -1 in $\mathbb{C} - \{0\}$ can be joined by the semi-circular path Γ with parametrization $\gamma(t) = e^{it}$ $(t \in [0, \pi])$. Sets with this property are called *connected*.

It turns out that many functions have domains which are both open and connected. We therefore devote this section to a discussion of these properties.

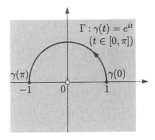

$\Gamma : \gamma(t) = e^{it}$
$(t \in [0, \pi])$

Figure 4.3

4.2 Open sets

In *Unit A1*, we defined open discs and open half-planes. In both cases no boundary points are included. More generally, an *open set* may be thought of as one which does not include any of its boundary points. The following definition, however, does not mention the boundary.

Definition   A set A in $\mathbb{C}$ is **open** if each point α in A is the centre of some open disc lying entirely in A (Figure 4.4).

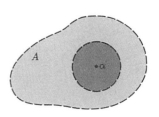

Figure 4.4

For example, the disc $D = \{z : |z| < 1\}$ is open because each point $\alpha \in D$ lies at a distance $1 - |\alpha| > 0$ from the boundary of D, and so the open disc

$$\{z : |z - \alpha| < 1 - |\alpha|\}$$

lies entirely in D (Figure 4.5).

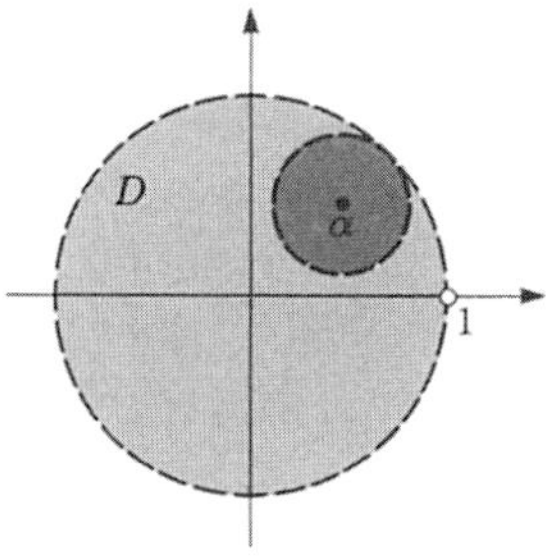

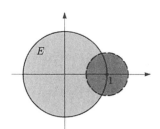

Figure 4.5

However, the disc $E = \{z : |z| \leq 1\}$ is *not* open; for example, the definition fails at $\alpha = 1$, since no open disc of the form

$$\{z : |z - 1| < r\}, \qquad r > 0,$$

lies entirely in E (Figure 4.6).

The same forms of argument show that every open disc is an open set and every closed disc is not an open set.

Also, note that every singleton set $\{\alpha\}$ is not open: no open disc centred on α lies entirely in $\{\alpha\}$.

Figure 4.6

Example 4.1

Prove that each of the following sets is open.

(a) $\{z : \operatorname{Re} z > 0\}$

(b) $\{z : |z| > 1\}$

(c) $\mathbb{C} - \{x \in \mathbb{R} : x \leq 0\}$

Solution

(a) Let $A = \{z : \operatorname{Re} z > 0\}$, so that the boundary of A is $\{z : \operatorname{Re} z = 0\}$. If $\alpha \in A$, then $\alpha = a + ib$, where $a > 0$, and the distance from α to the boundary of A is a. Hence the open disc

$$\{z : |z - \alpha| < a\}$$

lies entirely in A (Figure 4.7), so that A is open.

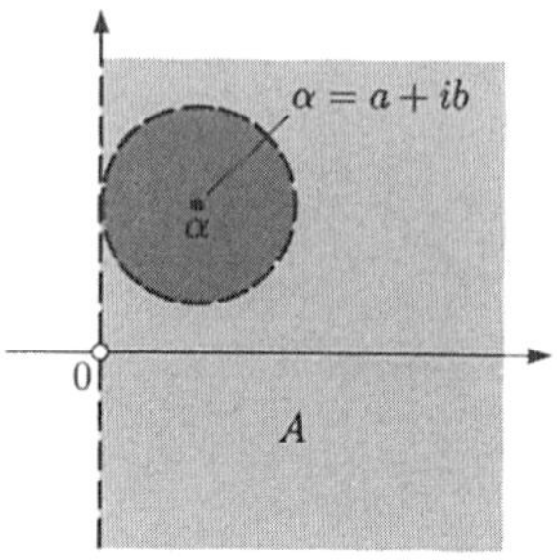

It follows similarly that every open half-plane is an open set.

(b) Let $A = \{z : |z| > 1\}$, so that the boundary of A is $\{z : |z| = 1\}$. If $\alpha \in A$, then $|\alpha| > 1$ and the distance from α to the boundary of A is $|\alpha| - 1 > 0$. Hence the open disc

$$\{z : |z - \alpha| < |\alpha| - 1\}$$

lies entirely in A (Figure 4.8), so that A is open.

Figure 4.7

$A = \mathbb{C} - \{z : |z| \leq 1\}$

(c) Let $A = \mathbb{C} - \{x \in \mathbb{R} : x \leq 0\}$, so that the boundary of A is $\{x \in \mathbb{R} : x \leq 0\}$. If $\alpha \in A$, then the distance from α to the boundary of A is

$$r_\alpha = \begin{cases} |\alpha|, & \operatorname{Re}\alpha \geq 0, \\ |\operatorname{Im}\alpha|, & \operatorname{Re}\alpha < 0. \end{cases}$$

Hence the open disc

$$\{z : |z - \alpha| < r_\alpha\}$$

lies entirely in A (Figure 4.9), so that A is open. ∎

Figure 4.8

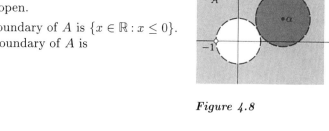

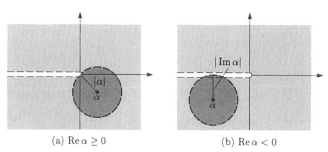

(a) $\operatorname{Re}\alpha \geq 0$ (b) $\operatorname{Re}\alpha < 0$

Figure 4.9   (a) $\operatorname{Re}\alpha \geq 0$ (b) $\operatorname{Re}\alpha < 0$

In each of these solutions we chose the radius of the open disc with centre α to be as large as possible, although there is no particular reason for doing this. For example, in Example 4.1(a), we could have taken the radius to be $\frac{1}{2}a$.

Problem 4.1

Prove that each of the following sets is open.

(a) $\mathbb{C} - \{0\}$

(b) $\{z : -2 < \operatorname{Re} z < 2, -1 < \operatorname{Im} z < 1\}$

(c) $\{z : 1 < |z| < 2\}$

(d) $\{z : \pi/3 < \operatorname{Arg} z < 2\pi/3\}$

You have now seen a number of different types of basic open sets: open discs, open half-planes, complements of closed discs, open annuli, open rectangles and open sectors. In addition, $\mathbb{C}$ is open. We note that the empty set $\varnothing$ is also considered to be open, because it contains no point α where the definition fails.

Now we describe two ways of creating 'new open sets from old'.

Theorem 4.1 Combination Rules

If A_1 and A_2 are open sets, then so are:

(a) $A_1 \cup A_2$ and

(b) $A_1 \cap A_2$.

Proof

(a) If $\alpha \in A_1 \cup A_2$, then α lies in A_1 or A_2 (or both); say, $\alpha \in A_1$. Since A_1 is open, there is a positive radius r such that

$$\{z : |z - \alpha| < r\} \subseteq A_1,$$

as indicated in Figure 4.10. Hence

$$\{z : |z - \alpha| < r\} \subseteq A_1 \cup A_2,$$

as required.

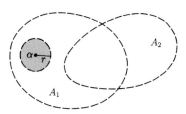

Figure 4.10

(b) If $\alpha \in A_1 \cap A_2$, then α lies in both A_1 and A_2. Since A_1, A_2 are both open, there are positive radii r_1, r_2 such that

$$\{z : |z - \alpha| < r_1\} \subseteq A_1 \quad \text{and} \quad \{z : |z - \alpha| < r_2\} \subseteq A_2,$$

as indicated in Figure 4.11. Thus if $r = \min\{r_1, r_2\}$, then

$$\{z : |z - \alpha| < r\} \subseteq A_1 \cap A_2,$$

as required. ∎

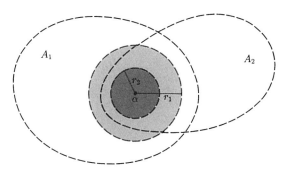

Figure 4.11

Applying Mathematical Induction to Theorem 4.1, we obtain the following corollary.

Corollary If $A_1, A_2, \ldots, A_n$ are open sets, then so are:

(a) $A_1 \cup A_2 \cup \ldots \cup A_n$ and

(b) $A_1 \cap A_2 \cap \ldots \cap A_n$.

Remark The proof of part(a) of Theorem 4.1 is readily adapted to show that the union of any (possibly infinite) collection of open sets is open. However, the intersection of an infinite collection of open sets need not be open. For example, if

$$A_n = \{z : |z| < 1/n\}, \qquad n = 1, 2, \ldots,$$

then each A_n is open, but

$$A_1 \cap A_2 \cap \ldots = \{z : z \in A_n, \text{ for } n = 1, 2, \ldots\}$$
$$= \{0\},$$

which is not open.

Problem 4.2

Use Theorem 4.1 or its corollary to prove that each of the following sets is open.

(a) $\{z : \operatorname{Re} z > 0, \operatorname{Im} z > 0, |z| < 1\}$

(b) $\{z : \operatorname{Re} z \neq 0\}$

4.3 Connected sets

In *Unit A2* we defined a path to be a subset Γ of $\mathbb{C}$ which is the image of an associated continuous function $\gamma : I \longrightarrow \mathbb{C}$ (the parametrization of Γ), where I is an interval of the real line. If $I = [a, b]$, then $\gamma(a)$ and $\gamma(b)$ are, respectively, called the initial point and final point of the path. The path Γ is said to **join** $\gamma(a)$ to $\gamma(b)$.

$\Gamma = \gamma(I)$

Now we use such paths to define the notion of a *connected set*.

Definition A set A in $\mathbb{C}$ is (**pathwise**) **connected** if each pair of points α, β in A can be joined by a path lying entirely in A.

The word 'pathwise' is usually omitted. It is included here because there is a more general notion of connectedness (which we do not require at this stage).

Figure 4.12 illustrates this definition. Note that the path shown in the figure avoids the 'hole' and so lies entirely in A.

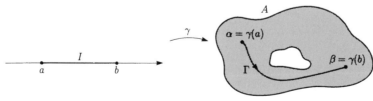

Figure 4.12

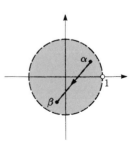

Figure 4.13

The open disc $D = \{z : |z| < 1\}$ is connected because any two points $\alpha, \beta \in D$ can be joined by, for example, the line segment from α to β, which lies entirely in D (Figure 4.13). Similarly, the closed disc $E = \{z : |z| \leq 1\}$ is connected.

Connected sets like the discs D and E in which any two points α and β can be joined by a line segment are called **convex**. Other examples of sets which are convex and, therefore, connected are any disc, half-plane or rectangle, and $\mathbb{C}$ itself.

However, not all connected sets are convex, as the following example shows.

Example 4.2

Prove that the set $\{z : |z| > 1\}$ is not convex, but is connected.

Solution

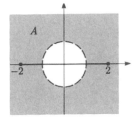

Figure 4.14

The set $A = \{z : |z| > 1\}$ is not convex because, for example, the interval $[-2, 2] \not\subseteq A$ (Figure 4.14). However, any two points α, β of A can be joined by a path in A. For example, if $|\alpha| = |\beta|$, then such a path Γ could be a circular arc, with centre 0, from α to β. If $|\alpha| \neq |\beta|$, then a suitable path Γ would consist of the (anticlockwise) circular arc, with centre 0, from α to $(|\alpha|/|\beta|)\beta$, followed by part of the ray from 0 through β (Figure 4.15). ∎

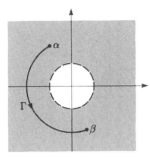 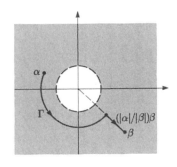

Figure 4.15   (a) $|\alpha| = |\beta|$ (b) $|\alpha| \neq |\beta|$

Remarks

1 In this solution we did not attempt to construct the simplest or shortest path from α to β. Rather, we chose a reasonably simple *type of path* which works for any pair α, β in A. Many other choices of path could be made; for example, we could take a path along the edge of a square through α, centred at 0, followed by a line segment to β.

2 Although we did not specify the parametrization of the path Γ joining α and β, this could be done if necessary. Suppose, for example, that $\alpha = 2i$ and $\beta = -4i$. Then the path

$$\Gamma_1 : \gamma_1(t) = 2e^{i\pi(t+1/2)} \qquad (t \in [0, 1])$$

has initial point $\gamma_1(0) = 2i$ and final point $\gamma_1(1) = -2i$, and the path

$$\Gamma_2 : \gamma_2(t) = -2ti \qquad (t \in [1, 2])$$

has initial point $\gamma_2(1) = -2i$ and final point $\gamma_2(2) = -4i$. Thus the path $\Gamma = \Gamma_1 \cup \Gamma_2$ with parametrization

$$\gamma(t) = \begin{cases} \gamma_1(t), & t \in [0, 1], \\ \gamma_2(t), & t \in [1, 2], \end{cases}$$

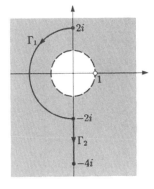

Figure 4.16

joins $2i$ to $-4i$ (Figure 4.16). The continuity of γ follows from that of γ_1 and γ_2, together with the fact that $\gamma_1(1) = \gamma_2(1)$.

Notice that we chose the domains of γ_1 and γ_2 to be adjacent intervals so that the domain of γ is an interval (as required by the definition of a path). It may require some ingenuity to 'glue' two or more parametrizations together in this way. Usually, a geometric description of such a path is sufficient.

3 The solution to Example 4.2 is readily adapted to prove the connectedness of other sets with rotational symmetry, such as $\mathbb{C} - \{0\}$ or an annulus.

Problem 4.3

Prove that each of the following sets is connected.

(a) $\mathbb{C} - \{x \in \mathbb{R} : x \le 0\}$ (b) $\{z : -1 < \operatorname{Re} z < 1 \text{ or } -1 < \operatorname{Im} z < 1\}$

Is either of the above sets convex?

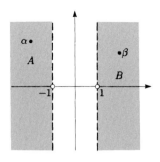

Figure 4.17 $A \cup B$ not connected

The property of connectedness is not preserved by forming unions or intersections. For example, if

$$A = \{z : \operatorname{Re} z < -1\} \quad \text{and} \quad B = \{z : \operatorname{Re} z > 1\},$$

then A and B are connected, but $A \cup B$ is not connected, since no point α in A can be joined to a point β in B by a path lying entirely in $A \cup B$ (Figure 4.17). Also, if

$$A = \{z : -1 < \operatorname{Re} z < 1\} \quad \text{and} \quad B = \{z : |z| > 2\},$$

then A and B are connected but $A \cap B$ is not (Figure 4.18).

The following problem does give one rule for obtaining 'new connected sets from old', but in practice it is usually easier to argue directly from the definition.

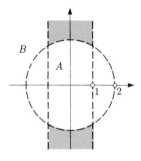

Problem 4.4

Prove that if A and B are connected and $A \cap B \ne \varnothing$, then $A \cup B$ is connected.

Figure 4.18 $A \cap B$ not connected

Another general property of connected sets is given by the following result. It will be of theoretical importance later in the course.

Theorem 4.2 Let f be a continuous function whose domain A is connected. Then the image $f(A)$ is also connected.

'The continuous image of a connected set is connected.'

Proof   We want to show that each pair of points in $f(A)$ can be joined by a path in $f(A)$. Such a pair of points must be of the form $f(\alpha), f(\beta)$, where $\alpha, \beta \in A$.

Because the set A is connected, we can join α, β by a path Γ in A, which is parametrized by a continuous function

$$\gamma : [a, b] \longrightarrow A, \quad \text{with } \gamma(a) = \alpha, \gamma(b) = \beta,$$

as shown on the left-hand side of Figure 4.19.

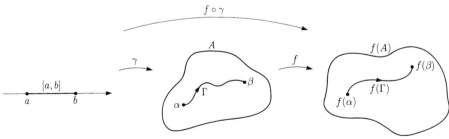

Figure 4.19

Now consider the function $f \circ \gamma : [a, b] \longrightarrow f(A)$ shown in Figure 4.19. Then $f \circ \gamma$ is continuous, by the Composition Rule, and

$$(f \circ \gamma)(a) = f(\gamma(a)) = f(\alpha),$$
$$(f \circ \gamma)(b) = f(\gamma(b)) = f(\beta).$$

Hence $f(\alpha), f(\beta)$ are joined in $f(A)$ by the path

$$f(\Gamma) = (f \circ \gamma)([a, b])$$
$$\subseteq f(A). \quad \blacksquare$$

Note that the continuous image of an open set need *not* be open; for example, the function $f(z) = 0$ $(z \in \mathbb{C})$ is continuous but $f(\mathbb{C}) = \{0\}$ is not open.

4.4 Regions

As noted earlier, the domains of many complex functions are both open and connected. It is useful, therefore, to introduce a name for such sets.

Definition A **region** is a non-empty, connected, open set.

Note that $\varnothing$ is not a region.

In Subsections 4.2 and 4.3 you saw many examples of sets which are both open and connected. For future reference, we present a list of basic types of region.

Basic Regions

The following subsets of $\mathbb{C}$ are regions:

(a) any open disc;
(b) any open half-plane;
(c) the complement of any closed disc;
(d) any open annulus;
(e) any open rectangle;
(f) any open sector (including cut planes);
(g) the set $\mathbb{C}$ itself.

We often encounter domains of functions which *are* regions but which do not fall within this basic list. For example, the domain of $f(z) = \tan z$,

$$\mathbb{C} - \left\{ \left(n + \tfrac{1}{2}\right) \pi : n \in \mathbb{Z} \right\},$$

is both open and connected and therefore a region.

See Problem 4.5.

In most cases it is straightforward to verify directly that the set is open and connected. However, one general result is sometimes useful.

Theorem 4.3 If $\mathcal{R}$ is a region and $\alpha_0 \in \mathcal{R}$, then $\mathcal{R} - \{\alpha_0\}$ is also a region.

To avoid confusion with other uses of the letter R, we designate a general region by a special type face: $\mathcal{R}$.

Proof Since $\mathcal{R}$ is a region it contains an open disc centred on α_0; hence $\mathcal{R} - \{\alpha_0\}$ is non-empty.

Since

$$\mathcal{R} - \{\alpha_0\} = \mathcal{R} \cap (\mathbb{C} - \{\alpha_0\}),$$

we deduce that $\mathcal{R} - \{\alpha_0\}$ is open, by Theorem 4.1.

Now suppose that $\alpha, \beta \in \mathcal{R} - \{\alpha_0\}$. Since $\alpha, \beta \in \mathcal{R}$ and $\mathcal{R}$ is a region, we can join α and β by a path Γ in $\mathcal{R}$, and this path also lies in $\mathcal{R} - \{\alpha_0\}$ if $\alpha_0 \notin \Gamma$. If, however, Γ does contain α_0, then we choose an open disc

$$\{z : |z - \alpha_0| < r\} \subseteq \mathcal{R}$$

(which is possible since $\mathcal{R}$ is a region) and modify Γ inside this disc, in order to avoid α_0 (Figure 4.20). The resulting path joins α and β in $\mathcal{R} - \{\alpha_0\}$, so $\mathcal{R} - \{\alpha_0\}$ is connected. Therefore $\mathcal{R} - \{\alpha_0\}$ is a region. $\quad \blacksquare$

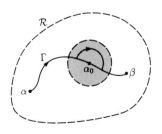

Figure 4.20 Modifying Γ to avoid α_0, by means of a circular arc

By applying Theorem 4.3 repeatedly, we deduce that if $\mathcal{R}$ is a region and $\alpha_1, \alpha_2, \ldots, \alpha_n \in \mathcal{R}$, then $\mathcal{R} - \{\alpha_1, \alpha_2, \ldots, \alpha_n\}$ is also a region. For example,

$$\mathcal{R} = \mathbb{C} - \{-\pi/2, \pi/2\}$$

is a region. It is tempting to think that Theorem 4.3 can be used to deduce that the domain of $f(z) = \tan z$, namely

$$\mathbb{C} - \left\{\left(n + \tfrac{1}{2}\right)\pi : n \in \mathbb{Z}\right\},$$

is a region. However, in this case we are removing from $\mathbb{C}$ an *infinite* set of points, and so the result does not follow immediately. For this example, it is necessary to work directly from the definition of a region, which we now ask you to do.

Problem 4.5

Prove that $\mathcal{R} = \mathbb{C} - \left\{\left(n + \tfrac{1}{2}\right)\pi : n \in \mathbb{Z}\right\}$ is a region.

5 THE EXTREME VALUE THEOREM

After working through this section, you should be able to:

(a) determine whether or not a given subset of $\mathbb{C}$ is: *closed, bounded*;

(b) explain the statement 'E is a compact subset of $\mathbb{C}$';

(c) state the Extreme Value Theorem and use its corollary, the Boundedness Theorem, to prove that certain functions are bounded on compact sets;

(d) identify the *interior, exterior* and *boundary* of a given subset of $\mathbb{C}$.

5.1 Compact sets

Given a real function $f : \mathbb{R} \to \mathbb{R}$, we often wish to determine the extreme values (that is, the absolute maximum and minimum values) of the function on a given interval I. For example, if

$$f(x) = x^2 \quad \text{and} \quad I = [-1, 2],$$

then the maximum value of f on I is $f(2) = 4$ and the minimum value of f on I is $f(0) = 0$ (Figure 5.1).

It is natural to seek a general result which states that certain types of functions *always* attain maximum and minimum values on certain types of interval. The examples in Figure 5.2 indicate that such a result cannot hold if we allow f to be discontinuous, or if we allow I to be an open interval.

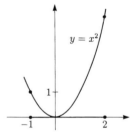

Figure 5.1

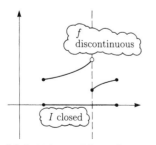

(a) f attains a minimum but not a maximum value on I

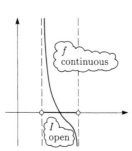

(b) f attains neither a minimum nor a maximum value on I

Figure 5.2

However, if we insist that f is continuous and that $I = [a, b]$ is a closed interval with finite endpoints (in the domain of f), then f must attain maximum and minimum values on I. This result, from real analysis, is called the Extreme Value Theorem.

Our aim in this final section of the unit is to obtain a version of the Extreme Value Theorem which applies to complex functions. We have already introduced the idea of a continuous complex function and so it remains to determine the appropriate type of subset of $\mathbb{C}$ with which to replace the closed interval $I = [a, b]$.

Section 2

One good candidate for such a type of subset is a closed disc

$$\{z : |z - \alpha| \le r\}, \qquad \alpha \in \mathbb{C}, r > 0.$$

Such a set includes its boundary points, so that the type of counter-example illustrated in Figure 5.2(b) is not possible. More generally, we define a new type of set which has the property of including all its boundary points. Such sets can most neatly be defined as follows.

The terms 'boundary point' and 'boundary', for which we have not yet required precise meanings, are defined formally at the end of this subsection.

Definition   A set E in $\mathbb{C}$ is **closed** if its complement $\mathbb{C} - E$ is open.

Thus, to prove that a set E is closed we must show that its complement is open.

Example 5.1

Prove that each of the following sets is closed.

(a) $\{z : \operatorname{Re} z \le 0\}$ (b) $\{z : |z| \le 1\}$ (c) $\{0\}$

Solution

In Example 4.1(a) and (b) and Problem 4.1(a) we showed that the complement of each of these sets is open, as required. ∎

More generally, any closed half-plane or closed disc is a closed set; further examples are given in the following problem.

Problem 5.1 _____

Prove that each of the following sets is closed.

(a) $\{z : |z| \ge 1\}$ (b) $\{z : |z| = 1\}$

As for open sets, we can obtain 'new closed sets from old ones' by using the following Combination Rules.

Theorem 5.1 Combination Rules

If E_1 and E_2 are closed sets, then so are

(a) $E_1 \cup E_2$ and

(b) $E_1 \cap E_2$.

Proof Since E_1 and E_2 are closed, we know that $\mathbb{C} - E_1$ and $\mathbb{C} - E_2$ are open. Now

$$\mathbb{C} - (E_1 \cup E_2) = (\mathbb{C} - E_1) \cap (\mathbb{C} - E_2)$$

and

$$\mathbb{C} - (E_1 \cap E_2) = (\mathbb{C} - E_1) \cup (\mathbb{C} - E_2),$$

and hence these sets are both open, by Theorem 4.1. Thus the result follows. ∎

These two properties of sets are known as de Morgan's Laws. They can be checked by drawing Venn diagrams.

For example, by Theorem 5.1(b), the circle

$$E = \{z : |z| = 1\}$$

is closed because it is the intersection of the two closed sets

$$\{z : |z| \leq 1\} \quad \text{and} \quad \{z : |z| \geq 1\}.$$

The following corollary extends Theorem 5.1 to any finite number of sets.

Corollary If $E_1, E_2, \ldots, E_n$ are closed sets, then so are
(a) $E_1 \cup E_2 \cup \cdots \cup E_n$ and
(b) $E_1 \cap E_2 \cap \cdots \cap E_n$.

Problem 5.2

Use Theorem 5.1 or its corollary to prove that each of the following sets is closed.
(a) $\{z : -1 \leq \operatorname{Re} z \leq 1, -1 \leq \operatorname{Im} z \leq 1\}$ (b) $\{z : \operatorname{Im} z = 0\}$

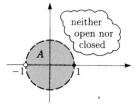

Figure 5.3

Warning If a set contains some but not all of its boundary points, then it is *neither* open *nor* closed. For example, the set

$$A = \{z : |z| < 1\} \cup \{1\},$$

shown in Figure 5.3, is not open (because no disc $\{z : |z - 1| < r\}$ lies entirely in A) and it is not closed (because its complement is not open: no disc $\{z : |z - 1| < r\}$ lies entirely in $\mathbb{C} - A$). On the other hand, since the sets $\mathbb{C}$ and $\varnothing$ are both open, they are also both closed (being complementary).

The other new concept which we need is that of a *bounded* set.

Definition A set E in $\mathbb{C}$ is **bounded** if it is contained in some closed disc. A set is **unbounded** if it is not bounded.

For example, every open disc or closed disc is bounded, but every half-plane is unbounded.

Problem 5.3

Which of the following sets are closed and which are bounded?
(a) $\{z : |z| = 1\}$ (b) $\{z : \operatorname{Im} z = 0\}$
(c) $\{z : -1 < \operatorname{Re} z < 1, -1 < \operatorname{Im} z < 1\}$

It turns out that the appropriate conditions for a set E (on which a function f is continuous) to satisfy, in order that the Extreme Value Theorem holds, are that E is closed and bounded. It is convenient, therefore, to give such sets a name; they are called *compact*.

> **Definition** A set E in $\mathbb{C}$ is **compact** if E is closed and bounded.

This is one of several equivalent definitions of compactness for subsets of $\mathbb{C}$ discussed in texts on point-set topology.

For example, every circle is compact, every closed disc is compact, but every open disc is not compact (not being closed), and every half-plane is not compact (not being bounded).

As the name suggests, compact sets should be thought of as 'neat and tidy' — they are not too large (being bounded) and have no 'loose ends' (since none of their boundaries has been left out).

Problem 5.4

Prove that the set

$$\{z : -1 \le \operatorname{Re} z \le 1, -1 \le \operatorname{Im} z \le 1\}$$

is compact.

We are now in a position to state a version of the Extreme Value Theorem for complex functions.

> ### Theorem 5.2 Extreme Value Theorem
>
> Let the function f be continuous on a compact set E. Then there are numbers α and β in E such that
>
> $$|f(\beta)| \le |f(z)| \le |f(\alpha)|, \qquad \text{for all } z \in E.$$

The proof of the Extreme Value Theorem is deferred to the next subsection, since it is rather involved.

Figure 5.4 shows the geometric interpretation of the Extreme Value Theorem: the image $f(E)$ lies in the set

$$\{w : |f(\beta)| \le |w| \le |f(\alpha)|\}.$$

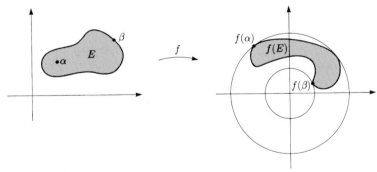

Figure 5.4

Note that, as indicated in Figure 5.4, the numbers α and β need not be unique.

It can often be extremely difficult to determine the maximum and minimum values of $|f(z)|$ on a given compact set. However, in many applications we do not need the actual maximum and minimum values. It is often enough to know that the function f is **bounded** on E; that is, the image $f(E)$ is a bounded set. If f is continuous on E, then this follows immediately from the Extreme Value Theorem.

Theorem 5.3 Boundedness Theorem

Let the function f be continuous on a compact set E. Then there is a number M such that

$$|f(z)| \leq M, \qquad \text{for all } z \in E. \tag{*}$$

For a given function f and set E, we can often find an explicit value of M such that the statement (*) holds. For example, if

$$f(z) = z^3 + 2z - i \quad \text{and} \quad E = \{z : |z| \leq 1\},$$

then, for all z in E,

$$\begin{aligned} |f(z)| &= |z^3 + 2z - i| \\ &\leq |z|^3 + 2|z| + 1, \qquad \text{by the Triangle Inequality,} \\ &\leq 1 + 2 + 1 = 4, \qquad \text{since } |z| \leq 1. \end{aligned}$$

However, the Boundedness Theorem can be applied even when the formula for f is complicated or unknown — as long as f is continuous.

Problem 5.5

In each of the following cases, prove that the given function f is bounded on the given set E by using Theorem 5.3 *and* by explicit estimation.

(a) $f(z) = e^{1/z}$, $\quad E = \{z : |z| = \frac{1}{2}\}$

(b) $f(z) = \sin z$, $\quad E = \{z : |z| \leq 27\}$

(c) $f(z) = \dfrac{z^2 + 1}{z - 2i}$, $\quad E = \{z : -1 \leq \operatorname{Re} z \leq 1, -1 \leq \operatorname{Im} z \leq 1\}$

Figure 5.4 suggests that if E is compact and f is continuous on E, then the image $f(E)$ is also compact. This is indeed the case, as we now prove.

Theorem 5.4 If the function f is continuous on a compact set E, then $f(E)$ is compact.

'The continuous image of a compact set is compact.'

Proof We know, by the Extreme Value Theorem, that $f(E)$ is bounded. Thus we need prove only that $f(E)$ is closed; that is, $\mathbb{C} - f(E)$ is open.

Suppose, therefore, that $\alpha \in \mathbb{C} - f(E)$. We want to find an open disc centred at α which lies entirely in $\mathbb{C} - f(E)$ (see Figure 5.5). To do this, consider the function

$$g(z) = f(z) - \alpha,$$

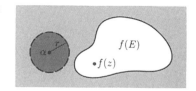

Figure 5.5

which is non-zero on E (since $f(z) \neq \alpha$, for $z \in E$) and continuous there. By the Extreme Value Theorem, there exists $\beta \in E$ such that

$$|g(z)| \geq |g(\beta)|, \qquad \text{for all } z \in E;$$

that is,

$$|f(z) - \alpha| \geq r, \qquad \text{for all } z \in E,$$

where $r = |g(\beta)| > 0$. So the open disc with centre α and radius r lies in $\mathbb{C} - f(E)$, as required. ∎

The boundary of a set

So far we have treated the concept of the boundary of a set rather informally. It has been easy to 'see' what the boundary is; for example, the circle $\{z : |z| = 1\}$ is the boundary of the open disc $\{z : |z| < 1\}$. However, this concept can be made precise (and we shall need this precision later in the course), and we now do this. First, we identify two types of point which are definitely not boundary points.

Definitions   Let A be a subset of $\mathbb{C}$ and let $\alpha \in \mathbb{C}$. Then

(a) α is an **interior point** of A if there is an open disc centred at α which lies entirely in A;

(b) α is an **exterior point** of A if there is an open disc centred at α which lies entirely outside A.

The set of interior points of A forms the **interior** of A, written int A, and the set of exterior points of A forms the **exterior** of A, written ext A.

For example, if $A = \{z : |z| < 1\}$, then

$$\text{int } A = \{z : |z| < 1\} = A \text{ and } \text{ext } A = \{z : |z| > 1\}.$$

The definitions are illustrated in Figures 5.6 and 5.7 for $A = \{z : |z| < 1\}$.

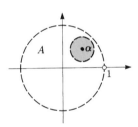

Figure 5.6 $\alpha \in \text{int } A$

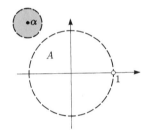

Figure 5.7 $\alpha \in \text{ext } A$

If α is neither an interior point nor an exterior point of A, then each open disc centred at α must meet both A and $\mathbb{C} - A$. Points with this property do qualify as boundary points.

Definitions   Let A be a subset of $\mathbb{C}$ and let $\alpha \in \mathbb{C}$. Then α is a **boundary point** of A if each open disc centred at α contains at least one point of A and at least one point of $\mathbb{C} - A$.

The set of boundary points of A forms the **boundary** of A, written ∂A.

∂A may be read as 'delta A'.

It follows from this definition that int A, ext A and ∂A are disjoint sets, and that

$$\partial A = \mathbb{C} - (\text{int } A \cup \text{ext } A).$$

Thus, once you have removed int A and ext A from $\mathbb{C}$, what is left is ∂A. For example, if $A = \{z : |z| < 1\}$, then

$$\partial A = \mathbb{C} - (\{z : |z| < 1\} \cup \{z : |z| > 1\})$$
$$= \{z : |z| = 1\},$$

as expected (see Figure 5.8).

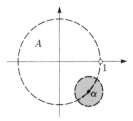

Figure 5.8 $\alpha \in \partial A$

Problem 5.6

For each of the following sets A, write down int A, ext A and ∂A.

(a) $A = \{z : |z| \leq 1\}$ (b) $A = \{x + iy : x < 0\}$

(c) $A = \mathbb{C} - \{0\}$ (d) $A = \{0\}$

You may have noticed in Problem 5.6 that, in each case, int A and ext A are open sets, whereas ∂A is closed. This is always true.

Theorem 5.5 If A is a subset of $\mathbb{C}$, then

(a) int A and ext A are open;

(b) ∂A is closed.

Proof

(a) If $\alpha \in$ int A, then there is an open disc $\{z : |z - \alpha| < r\}$ lying entirely in A. Since this disc is open, all points of it are interior points of A, and so

$$\{z : |z - \alpha| < r\} \subseteq \text{int } A.$$

Hence int A is open. A similar argument shows that ext A is open.

(b) By part (a), int A and ext A are open; hence, by Theorem 4.1, int $A \cup$ ext A is open. Since

$$\partial A = \mathbb{C} - (\text{int } A \cup \text{ext } A),$$

it follows that ∂A is closed. ∎

5.2 Proof of the Extreme Value Theorem

We begin with a lemma about closed sets.

This subsection may be omitted on a first reading.

Lemma 5.1 If E is a closed set and $\{z_n\}$ is a sequence in E with limit α, then $\alpha \in E$.

Proof Suppose, in fact, that $\alpha \in \mathbb{C} - E$. Since $\mathbb{C} - E$ is open, it contains an open disc $\{z : |z - \alpha| < r\}$, which in turn contains all but a finite number of the terms of $\{z_n\}$ (since $z_n \to \alpha$ as $n \to \infty$). However, this contradicts the fact that $\{z_n\}$ is in E. We conclude that $\alpha \in E$, as required. ∎

Remark The converse of Lemma 5.1 is also true. If the limit of each convergent sequence in the set E also lies in E, then E is closed. However, we do not need this converse result.

Next we need a fundamental result about nested closed rectangles (which will also be required later in the course). To prove this result we make use of the Monotone Convergence Theorem, a result from real analysis, which tells us that

> if the real sequence $\{a_n\}$ is increasing and bounded above, then $\{a_n\}$ is convergent.

In fact, this theorem also says that if $\{a_n\}$ is decreasing and bounded below, then $\{a_n\}$ is convergent.

Theorem 5.6 Nested Rectangles Theorem

Let $R_n, n = 0, 1, 2, \ldots$, be a sequence of closed rectangles with sides parallel to the axes, and with diagonals of lengths $s_n, n = 0, 1, 2, \ldots$, such that

1. $R_0 \supseteq R_1 \supseteq R_2 \supseteq \ldots$, and

2. $\lim_{n \to \infty} s_n = 0$.

Then there is a unique complex number α which lies in all of the rectangles R_n. Moreover, for each positive number ε, there is an integer N such that

$$R_n \subseteq \{z : |z - \alpha| < \varepsilon\}, \quad \text{for all } n > N. \tag{$*$}$$

This result is sometimes referred to as the Chinese Box Theorem.

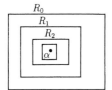

Figure 5.9

The last statement $(*)$ of the theorem says, roughly speaking, that the sequence of rectangles $\{R_n\}$ converges to the point $\{\alpha\}$ as $n \to \infty$, as indicated in Figure 5.9.

Proof Let

$$R_n = \{x + iy : a_n \le x \le c_n, b_n \le y \le d_n\}, \quad n = 0, 1, 2, \ldots,$$

as shown in Figure 5.10, so that

$$a_0 \le a_1 \le a_2 \le \ldots \le c_2 \le c_1 \le c_0, \tag{$\dagger$}$$
$$b_0 \le b_1 \le b_2 \le \ldots \le d_2 \le d_1 \le d_0.$$

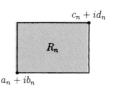

Figure 5.10

Thus the sequence $\{a_n\}$ is increasing and bounded above, by c_0, and so $\lim_{n \to \infty} a_n$ exists by the Monotone Convergence Theorem. Let $\lim_{n \to \infty} a_n = a$. Also, as shown in Figure 5.11,

$$0 \le c_n - a_n \le s_n, \quad \text{for } n = 0, 1, 2, \ldots,$$

so that $\lim_{n \to \infty} (c_n - a_n) = 0$, by the Squeeze Rule for sequences. Thus,

$$\begin{aligned} \lim_{n \to \infty} c_n &= \lim_{n \to \infty} (a_n + (c_n - a_n)) \\ &= \lim_{n \to \infty} a_n + \lim_{n \to \infty} (c_n - a_n) \\ &= a + 0 = a. \end{aligned}$$

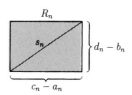

Figure 5.11

Likewise,

$$\lim_{n \to \infty} d_n = \lim_{n \to \infty} b_n = b,$$

for some real number b. Since, by $(\dagger)$,

$$a_n \le a \le c_n, \quad \text{for } n = 0, 1, 2, \ldots,$$
$$b_n \le b \le d_n, \quad \text{for } n = 0, 1, 2, \ldots,$$

it follows that $\alpha = a + ib \in R_n$, for all n.

Now if $z \in R_n$, then

$$|z - \alpha| \le s_n,$$

as indicated in Figure 5.12.

Figure 5.12 $|z - \alpha| \le s_n$

Since $s_n \to 0$ as $n \to \infty$, there is an integer N such that

$$s_n < \varepsilon, \quad \text{for all } n > N;$$

thus

$$|z - \alpha| < \varepsilon, \quad \text{for all } n > N \text{ and } z \in R_n.$$

Thus, statement $(*)$ follows.

To prove that α is the only point lying in all the rectangles R_n, suppose that $\beta \neq \alpha$ also has this property. Then $|\alpha - \beta|$ is positive and, by applying $(*)$ with $\varepsilon = |\alpha - \beta|$, we obtain a contradiction since, for this choice of ε,

$$R_n \subseteq \{z : |z - \alpha| < \varepsilon\}$$

implies that $\beta \notin R_n$. ∎

We are now in a position to prove the Extreme Value Theorem.

Theorem 5.2 Extreme Value Theorem

Let the function f be continuous on a compact set E. Then there are numbers α and β in E such that

$$|f(\beta)| \leq |f(z)| \leq |f(\alpha)|, \quad \text{for all } z \in E.$$

Proof We prove that there is a number α in E such that

$$|f(z)| \leq |f(\alpha)|, \quad \text{for all } z \in E.$$

Since E is bounded, we can choose a closed rectangle R_0, with diagonal length s_0 say, such that $E \subseteq R_0$. This rectangle R_0 can then be expressed as the union of four closed rectangles T_1, T_2, T_3 and T_4, each with diagonal length $\frac{1}{2}s_0$, using vertical and horizontal lines to bisect the sides of R_0 (Figure 5.13).

Since the proof that there is a number β in E such that

$$|f(\beta)| \leq |f(z)|, \quad \text{for all } z \in E,$$

is similar, we omit it.

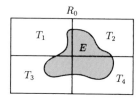

Figure 5.13

Claim At least one of the rectangles, T_j say, has the property that

for each $z \in E$ there is some $w \in E \cap T_j$ such that

$$|f(z)| \leq |f(w)|.$$

Indeed, if the rectangle T_j does not have this property, then there is a number z_j in E such that

$$|f(z_j)| > |f(w)|, \quad \text{for all } w \in E \cap T_j.$$

Thus, if the claim is false then such a number z_j exists for each $j = 1, 2, 3, 4$. It follows that

$$\max\{|f(z_1)|, |f(z_2)|, |f(z_3)|, |f(z_4)|\} > |f(w)|, \quad \text{for all } w \in E,$$

which is evidently a contradiction. Hence the claim is true. Now put $R_1 = T_j$ and repeat the process with $E \cap R_1$ instead of E.

Continuing indefinitely, we obtain a sequence $R_n, n = 0, 1, 2, \ldots$, of closed rectangles such that for $n = 0, 1, 2, \ldots$:

(a) $R_{n+1} \subseteq R_n$;

(b) R_n has diagonal length $\left(\frac{1}{2}\right)^n s_0$;

(c) for each $z \in E \cap R_n$ there is some w in $E \cap R_{n+1}$ such that

$$|f(z)| \leq |f(w)|.$$

By the Nested Rectangles Theorem we deduce that there is a unique point α lying in all the rectangles R_n. Moreover, for each positive number ε, there is an integer N such that

$$R_n \subseteq \{z : |z - \alpha| < \varepsilon\}, \quad \text{for all } n > N. \tag{$*$}$$

We claim that the number α lies in E and also that

$$|f(z)| \leq |f(\alpha)|, \quad \text{for all } z \in E,$$

as required.

To prove this claim, we take *any* number z_0 in E and then use property (c) above to choose a sequence $\{z_n\}$ such that

$$z_n \in E \cap R_n, \quad \text{for } n = 0, 1, 2, \ldots$$

and

$$|f(z_n)| \leq |f(z_{n+1})|, \quad \text{for } n = 0, 1, 2, \ldots . \tag{†}$$

It follows from (*), since $z_n \in R_n$ for each n, and $R_n \subseteq R_N$ for all $n \geq N$, that $z_n \to \alpha$ as $n \to \infty$; thus $\alpha \in E$ by Lemma 5.1, since E is closed. Furthermore, since f is continuous on E, it is continuous at α, and so we deduce that

$$\lim_{n \to \infty} |f(z_n)| = |f(\alpha)|.$$

Hence

$$|f(z_0)| \leq |f(\alpha)|,$$

by (†). Since z_0 was any point of E, the proof is complete. ∎

Note that $E = E \cap R_0$, since $E \subseteq R_0$.

Although it is easy to state, the Extreme Value Theorem is surprisingly tricky to prove and you should not be dispirited if you found the proof difficult. The central idea of the proof — namely, the repeated splitting of the rectangles into smaller ones will appear again when we prove Cauchy's Theorem, the 'main result' in complex analysis.

EXERCISES

Section 1

Exercise 1.1 Prove that the sequence $\{(1 + i)/(2n^2 - 1)\}$ is null by
(a) using the definition; (b) using the Squeeze Rule.

Exercise 1.2 Decide which of the following sequences are null, and justify your answers.

(a) $\left\{ \left(\dfrac{1}{2} + \dfrac{i}{2} \right)^n \right\}$ (b) $\left\{ \dfrac{1}{2} + \left(\dfrac{i}{2} \right)^n \right\}$ (c) $(1 + i)^n$

Exercise 1.3 Show that each of the following sequences is convergent and find its limit.

(a) $\left\{ 5 + \dfrac{i}{2n} \right\}$ (b) $\left\{ \dfrac{2n - i}{n^2} \right\}$ (c) $\left\{ \dfrac{n - i}{n + i} \right\}$

(d) $\left\{ \dfrac{n^3 + 3in - 2}{4n^3 - in^2} \right\}$ (e) $\left\{ \dfrac{(1 + i)^n + (\sqrt{3} - i)^n}{3(2 - 2i)^n - 1} \right\}$

Exercise 1.4 Decide which of the following sequences tend to infinity, and justify your answers.

(a) $\left\{ \dfrac{n}{i} \right\}$ (b) $\{e^{in}\}$ (c) $\left\{ \dfrac{(\sqrt{3} - i)^n - 1}{(1 + i)^n} \right\}$

Exercise 1.5 Prove that each of the following sequences is divergent.
(a) $\{(i - 1)^n\}$ (b) $\{e^{n\pi i}\}$ (c) $\{n \cos(n\pi i^n)\}$

Exercise 1.6 Suppose that the sequence $\{z_n\}$ consists of two subsequences $\{z_{m_k}\}$ and $\{z_{n_k}\}$ such that $\lim\limits_{k \to \infty} z_{m_k} = \alpha = \lim\limits_{k \to \infty} z_{n_k}$. Prove that

$$\lim_{n \to \infty} z_n = \alpha.$$

Section 2

Exercise 2.1 For each of the following functions, decide whether it is continuous or discontinuous at the point α and then use the appropriate strategy, based on the definition of continuity, to prove your decision.

(a) $f(z) = z^2, \quad \alpha = 2i$ (b) $f(z) = z^{1/3}, \quad \alpha = -1$

Exercise 2.2 Using the Combination Rules, the Composition Rule, the Restriction Rule and the list of basic continuous functions in Frame 18, prove that each of the following functions is continuous.

(a) $f(z) = 3z^3 + |z|\operatorname{Re} z$

(b) $f(z) = |\sin z|$

(c) $f(x) = 1 + x(i - 1) \quad\quad (x \in [0, 1])$

(d) $f(x) = \cos x + i \sin x \quad\quad (x \in [0, 2\pi])$

Exercise 2.3 Consider the function $f(z) = \theta$, where θ is the argument of z in the interval $[0, 2\pi[$. Write down the domain of f and prove that f is discontinuous at 1. At what other points is f discontinuous?

Exercise 2.4 Evaluate each of the following limits.

(a) $\displaystyle\lim_{n\to\infty} \operatorname{Log}(\pi + i/n)$

(b) $\displaystyle\lim_{n\to\infty} \exp\left(\frac{(2n + 1)\pi}{2n - 1} i\right)$

(c) $\displaystyle\lim_{n\to\infty} \cos\left(\frac{(1 + i)^n}{(2 + i)^n}\right)$

Section 3

Exercise 3.1 For each of the following points α and sets A, decide whether α is a limit point of A and, in those cases where α is a limit point of A, prove it by specifying a suitable sequence $\{z_n\}$ in $A - \{\alpha\}$ which converges to α.

(a) $\alpha = i, \quad A = \{z : |z| < 1\}$

(b) $\alpha = i, \quad A = \{z : \operatorname{Re} z > 1\}$

(c) $\alpha = 1, \quad A = \{z : \operatorname{Re} z + \operatorname{Im} z = 1\}$

Exercise 3.2 Determine whether or not each of the following limits (of functions) exists. For each one that does, evaluate the limit.

(a) $\displaystyle\lim_{z\to 3} \frac{z^3 - 27}{z - 3}$ (b) $\displaystyle\lim_{z\to -i} \frac{z^2 + 1}{z + i}$

(c) $\displaystyle\lim_{z\to i\pi} \left(e^z \sinh z + \frac{1}{z}\right)$ (d) $\displaystyle\lim_{z\to 1} \frac{1}{\operatorname{Im} z}$

(e) $\displaystyle\lim_{z\to i} \frac{\operatorname{Re} z}{\operatorname{Im} z}$ (f) $\displaystyle\lim_{z\to 0} \frac{\operatorname{Re} z}{\operatorname{Im} z}$

Exercise 3.3 Evaluate the following limit (using the method of Example 3.3).

$$\lim_{z\to 0} \cos\left(\frac{(z + 2)^2 - (4 + z)}{z}\right)$$

Section 4

Exercise 4.1 Sketch each of the following sets and in each case write down whether it is open, convex, connected, a region.

(a) $A = \{z : |z - i| < 2\}$ (b) $B = \{z : 1 \leq |z - 1| < 2\}$

(c) $C = \{z : \operatorname{Im} z < -1\}$ (d) $A \cap C$ (e) $A \cup C$

(f) $B \cap C$ (g) $A - \{0\}$

Exercise 4.2 Justify your answers to part (a) of Exercise 4.1.

Exercise 4.3 Prove that the domain of the function $f(z) = \operatorname{cosec} z$ is a region.

Section 5

Exercise 5.1 Determine which of the sets in Exercise 4.1 are bounded.

Exercise 5.2 Determine whether each of the following sets is closed.

(a) $\{z : |z - i| \geq 2\}$

(b) $\{z : |z - 1| < 1 \text{ or } |z - 1| \geq 2\}$

(c) $\{z : \operatorname{Im} z \leq -1\}$

Exercise 5.3 In each of the following cases *either* use Theorem 5.3 to prove that the given function f is bounded on the set E, *or* explain why Theorem 5.3 does not apply.

(a) $f(z) = \sinh z$, $E = \{z : |z| \leq 1\}$ (b) $f(z) = \operatorname{Log} z$, $E = \{z : |z| \leq 1\}$

(c) $f(z) = \cos z$, $E = \{z : \operatorname{Re} z \geq 1\}$ (d) $f(z) = \dfrac{1}{z}$, $E = \{z : 1 \leq |z| \leq 2\}$

(e) $f(z) = \dfrac{1}{z}$, $E = \{z : 0 < |z| \leq 2\}$ (f) $f(z) = \dfrac{1}{z}$, $E = \{z : |z| \geq 1\}$

Exercise 5.4 Write down the interior, exterior and boundary of the following set.

$$A = \{z : |z - 1| < 1 \text{ or } |z - 1| \geq 2\}$$

SOLUTIONS TO THE PROBLEMS

Section 1

1.1 (a)

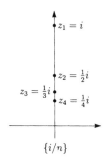

$$\{i/n\}$$

(b)

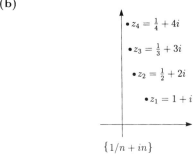

$$\{1/n + in\}$$

(c)

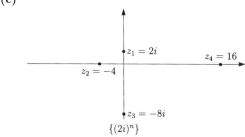

$$\{(2i)^n\}$$

1.2 (a) We want to show that
for each positive number ε, there is an integer N such that
$$\frac{1}{\sqrt{n}} < \varepsilon, \quad \text{for all } n > N. \qquad (*)$$
But we know that
$$\frac{1}{\sqrt{n}} < \varepsilon \iff \sqrt{n} > \frac{1}{\varepsilon}$$
$$\iff n > \frac{1}{\varepsilon^2}.$$
Therefore the statement $(*)$ holds if we take $N = [1/\varepsilon^2]$, and so $\{1/\sqrt{n}\}$ is a null sequence.

(b) We want to show that
for each positive number ε, there is an integer N such that
$$\left|\frac{1+i}{n}\right| < \varepsilon, \quad \text{for all } n > N. \qquad (*)$$
But we know that $|1+i| = \sqrt{2}$ and so
$$\left|\frac{1+i}{n}\right| < \varepsilon \iff \frac{\sqrt{2}}{n} < \varepsilon$$
$$\iff n > \frac{\sqrt{2}}{\varepsilon}.$$
Therefore the statement $(*)$ holds if we take $N = \left[\sqrt{2}/\varepsilon\right]$, and so $\{(1+i)/n\}$ is a null sequence.

1.3 (a) First note that
$$|0.6 + 0.8i| = ((0.6)^2 + (0.8)^2)^{1/2} = 1.$$
Hence
$$|z_n| = \left|\frac{(0.6 + 0.8i)^n}{n^2 + n}\right| = \frac{1}{n^2 + n}$$
$$\leq \frac{1}{n}, \quad \text{for } n = 1, 2, \dots.$$
Since $\{1/n\}$ is a null sequence, we deduce by the Squeeze Rule that $\{z_n\}$ is null also.

(b) Since $2^n \geq n$, for $n = 1, 2, \dots$,
$$\left|\left(\frac{i}{2}\right)^n\right| = \frac{1}{2^n} \leq \frac{1}{n}, \quad \text{for } n = 1, 2, \dots.$$
Since $\{1/n\}$ is a null sequence, we deduce by the Squeeze Rule that the sequence $\{(i/2)^n\}$ is null also.

1.4 (a) The dominant term is n^3, so we divide the numerator and denominator of z_n by it:
$$z_n = \frac{n^3 + 2in^2 + 3}{in^3 + 1} = \frac{1 + 2i/n + 3/n^3}{i + 1/n^3}.$$
Since $\{1/n\}$ and $\{1/n^3\}$ are basic null sequences,
$$\lim_{n \to \infty} z_n = \frac{1 + 0 + 0}{i + 0} = -i,$$
by the Combination Rules.

(b) Since $|3 + i| = \sqrt{10}$, $|2 + 2i| = \sqrt{8}$, $|1 + 2i| = \sqrt{5}$, the dominant term is $(3 + i)^n$, so we divide the numerator and denominator of z_n by it:
$$z_n = \frac{(3+i)^n + (2+2i)^n}{(1+2i)^n + 2(3+i)^n} = \frac{1 + ((2+2i)/(3+i))^n}{((1+2i)/(3+i))^n + 2}.$$
Since
$$|(2+2i)/(3+i)| = \sqrt{8}/\sqrt{10} < 1 \text{ and}$$
$$|(1+2i)/(3+i)| = \sqrt{5}/\sqrt{10} < 1,$$
both $\{((2+2i)/(3+i))^n\}$ and $\{((1+2i)/(3+i))^n\}$ are basic null sequences, and so
$$\lim_{n \to \infty} z_n = \frac{1 + 0}{0 + 2} = \frac{1}{2},$$
by the Combination Rules.

1.5 Since $\lim_{n \to \infty} x_n = a$ and $\lim_{n \to \infty} y_n = b$, it follows from the Combination Rules that
$$\lim_{n \to \infty} (x_n + iy_n) = \left(\lim_{n \to \infty} x_n\right) + i\left(\lim_{n \to \infty} y_n\right) = a + ib,$$
as required.

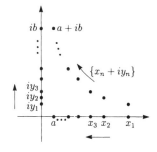

1.6 Let $z_n = n^3 - in^2 + (1+i)n$, for $n = 1, 2, \ldots$. Then

$$\frac{1}{z_n} = \frac{1}{n^3 - in^2 + (1+i)n}$$

$$= \frac{1/n^3}{1 - i/n + (1+i)/n^2}, \quad \text{for } n = 1, 2, \ldots.$$

Since $\{1/n\}$, $\{1/n^2\}$ and $\{1/n^3\}$ are basic null sequences, we deduce that

$$\lim_{n \to \infty} \frac{1}{z_n} = \frac{0}{1 - 0 + 0} = 0,$$

by the Combination Rules. Hence the sequence $\{z_n\}$ tends to infinity, by the Reciprocal Rule.

1.7 (a) $\dfrac{2i}{3}, \dfrac{4i}{5}, \dfrac{6i}{7}, \dfrac{8i}{9};$

(b) $\dfrac{3i}{4}, \dfrac{7i}{8}, \dfrac{11i}{12}, \dfrac{15i}{16};$

(c) $\dfrac{i}{2}, \dfrac{4i}{5}, \dfrac{9i}{10}, \dfrac{16i}{17}.$

1.8 (a) By inspection, the terms of the sequence $\{i^n\}$ are

$$i, -1, -i, 1, i, -1, -i, 1, \ldots.$$

Thus $\{i^n\}$ seems to have four convergent subsequences with different limits. In particular, for $k = 1, 2, \ldots$,

$$i^{4k} = \left(i^4\right)^k = 1^k = 1 \quad \text{and} \quad i^{4k+1} = i^{4k}i = i,$$

so that if $z_n = i^n$, then

$$\lim_{k \to \infty} z_{4k} = 1 \quad \text{and} \quad \lim_{k \to \infty} z_{4k+1} = i.$$

Hence, by the First Subsequence Rule, the sequence $\{z_n\}$ is divergent.

(b) The first few terms of the sequence

$$z_n = n^2 \sin\left(\frac{1}{3}n\pi\right), \quad n = 1, 2, \ldots,$$

are

$$\frac{\sqrt{3}}{2}, \frac{4\sqrt{3}}{2}, 0, \frac{-16\sqrt{3}}{2}, \frac{-25\sqrt{3}}{2}, 0, \frac{49\sqrt{3}}{2}, \ldots.$$

Now $\sin\left(\frac{1}{3}n\pi\right) = \frac{\sqrt{3}}{2}$ whenever $\frac{1}{3}n\pi$ is of the form $2k\pi + \pi/3$, $k = 1, 2, \ldots$; that is, whenever $n = 6k + 1$. The subsequence $\{z_{6k+1}\}$ of $\{z_n\}$, for which

$$z_{6k+1} = (6k+1)^2 \frac{\sqrt{3}}{2}, \quad k = 1, 2, \ldots,$$

tends to infinity (by the Reciprocal Rule: $1/((6k+1)^2\sqrt{3}/2) \to 0$ as $k \to \infty$). Hence the sequence $\{z_n\}$ is divergent by the Second Subsequence Rule.

Section 2

2.1 If $\lim_{n \to \infty} z_n = i$, then, by the Combination Rules,

$$\lim_{n \to \infty} \left(z_n^2 + 3z_n\right) = \left(\lim_{n \to \infty} z_n\right)^2 + 3 \lim_{n \to \infty} z_n$$

$$= i^2 + 3i$$

$$= -1 + 3i.$$

2.2 If $z_n = e^{i(\pi + 1/n)}$, $n = 1, 2, \ldots$, then, from the diagram, it appears that $\lim_{n \to \infty} z_n = -1$, as we show below.

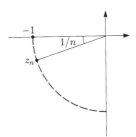

Since the arc length along the unit circle $|z| = 1$ from z_n to -1 has length $1/n$ and the line segment from z_n to -1 must be shorter, we have

$$|z_n - (-1)| \leq \frac{1}{n},$$

and hence $\{z_n - (-1)\}$ is a null sequence, by the Squeeze Rule. Thus

$$\lim_{n \to \infty} z_n = -1.$$

Now $\operatorname{Arg} z_n = -(\pi - 1/n) = -\pi + 1/n$, and hence

$$\lim_{n \to \infty} \operatorname{Arg} z_n = -\pi \quad \text{(Sum Rule)}.$$

The value of $\operatorname{Arg}(-1)$ is π.

2.3 (a) To prove that the function $f(z) = 1$ is continuous at each $\alpha \in \mathbb{C}$, we want to prove that

$$z_n \to \alpha \implies f(z_n) \to f(\alpha). \qquad (*)$$

But $f(z_n) = 1$, for $n = 1, 2, \ldots$, and $f(\alpha) = 1$, so the statement $(*)$ holds. Hence f is continuous.

(b) To prove that the function $f(z) = z$ is continuous at each $\alpha \in \mathbb{C}$, we want to prove that

$$z_n \to \alpha \implies f(z_n) \to f(\alpha). \qquad (*)$$

But $f(z_n) = z_n$, for $n = 1, 2, \ldots$, and $f(\alpha) = \alpha$, so the statement $(*)$ holds. Hence f is continuous.

(c) To prove that the function $f(z) = \overline{z}$ is continuous at each $\alpha \in \mathbb{C}$, we want to prove that

$$z_n \to \alpha \implies f(z_n) \to f(\alpha). \qquad (*)$$

But $f(z_n) = \overline{z_n}$, for $n = 1, 2, \ldots$, and $f(\alpha) = \overline{\alpha}$, so the statement $(*)$ follows from Theorem 1.4(b). Hence f is continuous.

(d), (e) and (f). These follow from Theorem 1.4(c), (d), (a), respectively, as in part (c).

2.4 To prove that the function $f(z) = \operatorname{Arg} z$ is discontinuous at each $\alpha \in \mathbb{R}$, with $\alpha < 0$, we must find one sequence $\{z_n\}$ in $\mathbb{C} - \{0\}$, the domain of f, such that

$$z_n \to \alpha \quad \text{but} \quad f(z_n) \not\to f(\alpha).$$

Following Problem 2.2, as discussed in Frame 6, we choose

$$z_n = |\alpha|e^{i(\pi + 1/n)}, \quad n = 1, 2, \ldots.$$

Then $z_n \to \alpha$ (by the Multiple Rule), and

$$\lim_{n \to \infty} \operatorname{Arg} z_n = \lim_{n \to \infty} (-\pi + 1/n) = -\pi.$$

But $\operatorname{Arg} \alpha = \pi$ and so $\lim_{n \to \infty} \operatorname{Arg} z_n \neq \operatorname{Arg} \alpha$. Hence $f(z) = \operatorname{Arg} z$ is discontinuous at each $\alpha \in \mathbb{R}$, with $\alpha < 0$.

2.5 **(a)** If $h(z) = -z^2$ and $g(z) = e^z$, then both h and g are basic continuous functions. Hence the function

$$f(z) = g(h(z)) = e^{-z^2}$$

is continuous by the Composition Rule.

(b) The function

$$g(z) = \frac{z^2 + i}{z^2 - i}$$

is a rational function and hence continuous. The domain of g contains the real line (since $z^2 - i \neq 0$ for $z \in \mathbb{R}$) and hence the function

$$f(x) = \frac{x^2 + i}{x^2 - i} \quad (x \in \mathbb{R}),$$

which is the restriction of g to $\mathbb{R}$, is continuous, by the Restriction Rule.

(c) The function $g(z) = |z|$ is a continuous function and the (real) function $h(x) = \log_e x$ is continuous, with domain $]0, \infty[$. Since g is continuous at each $\alpha \in \mathbb{C}$ and $g(z) > 0$ if $z \neq 0$, the function

$$f(z) = h(g(z)) = \log_e |z|$$

is continuous on $\mathbb{C} - \{0\}$, by the Composition Rule.

(d) The functions $g(z) = \operatorname{Re} z$, $h(z) = z^2 + 1$, $k(z) = |z|$ are continuous functions. Hence

$$z \longmapsto \operatorname{Re} \left(z^2 + 1 \right)$$

is continuous, by the Composition Rule, and

$$z \longmapsto |z|^2$$

is continuous, by the Product Rule.

Hence the function

$$f(z) = \operatorname{Re} \left(z^2 + 1 \right) - |z|^2$$

is continuous, by the Combination Rules.

2.6 The function $g(z) = (z^2 + 1)/(z - 2i)$ is a rational function and hence continuous on $\mathbb{C} - \{2i\}$.

The function $h(z) = \sin z$ is a basic continuous function. Hence, by the Composition Rule, the function

$$h(g(z)) = \sin \left(\frac{z^2 + 1}{z - 2i} \right)$$

is continuous on $\mathbb{C} - \{2i\}$.

The function

$$f(z) = \sin \left(\frac{z^2 + 1}{z - 2i} \right) \quad (z \in A),$$

where $A = \{z : -1 \leq \operatorname{Re} z \leq 1, -1 \leq \operatorname{Im} z \leq 1\}$, is the restriction of $h \circ g$ to A and $h \circ g$ is continuous on $\mathbb{C} - \{2i\}$; hence, by the Restriction Rule, the function f is continuous (on A).

2.7 **(a)** The sequence

$$z_n = \pi - 2/n, \quad n = 1, 2, \ldots,$$

has limit π (Sum and Multiple Rules), and π is a point at which the function $f(z) = \sin z$ is continuous. Hence

$$\lim_{n \to \infty} \sin(\pi - 2/n) = \sin \pi = 0.$$

(b) The sequence

$$z_n = i + 1/n^2, \quad n = 1, 2, \ldots,$$

has limit i (Sum Rule), and i is a point at which the function $f(z) = \operatorname{Arg} z$ is continuous. Hence

$$\lim_{n \to \infty} \operatorname{Arg} \left(i + 1/n^2 \right) = \operatorname{Arg} i = \pi/2.$$

(c) The sequence

$$z_n = -i\pi/2 + i/(2n), \quad n = 1, 2, \ldots,$$

has limit $-i\pi/2$ (Sum and Multiple Rules), and $-i\pi/2$ is a point at which the function $f(z) = \exp z$ is continuous. Hence

$$\lim_{n \to \infty} \exp(-i\pi/2 + i/(2n)) = \exp(-i\pi/2) = -i.$$

2.8 **(a)** Let $\alpha \in \{x \in \mathbb{R} : x < 0\}$. To prove that the function $g(z) = z^{1/2}$ is discontinuous at α, we must find a sequence z_n in $\mathbb{C}$ (the domain of g) such that

$$z_n \to \alpha \quad \text{but} \quad g(z_n) \nrightarrow g(\alpha).$$

Consider the sequence

$$z_n = |\alpha| e^{i(\pi + 1/n)}, \quad n = 1, 2, \ldots;$$

then, as we know from Problems 2.2 and 2.4, $z_n \to \alpha$. In terms of the principal argument,

$$z_n = |\alpha| e^{i(-\pi + 1/n)},$$

and so $|z_n| = |\alpha|$ and $\operatorname{Arg} z_n = -\pi + 1/n$. Thus

$$\begin{aligned}
g(z_n) &= z_n^{1/2} \\
&= \exp \left(\tfrac{1}{2} \operatorname{Log} z_n \right) \\
&= \exp \left(\log_e |z_n|^{1/2} + i(\operatorname{Arg} z_n)/2 \right) \\
&= \exp \left(\log_e |\alpha|^{1/2} \right) \exp(i(-\pi + 1/n)/2) \\
&= |\alpha|^{1/2} \exp(-i\pi/2 + i/(2n)).
\end{aligned}$$

Now, by Problem 2.7(c),

$$\exp(-i\pi/2 + i/(2n)) \to \exp(-i\pi/2) = -i.$$

Thus, by the Multiple Rule,

$$g(z_n) \to -|\alpha|^{1/2} i.$$

But

$$\begin{aligned}
g(\alpha) &= \alpha^{1/2} \\
&= \exp \left(\tfrac{1}{2} \operatorname{Log} \alpha \right) \\
&= \exp \left(\log_e |\alpha|^{1/2} + i(\operatorname{Arg} \alpha)/2 \right) \\
&= |\alpha|^{1/2} \exp(i\pi/2) \\
&= |\alpha|^{1/2} i.
\end{aligned}$$

Hence $g(z_n) \to -g(\alpha)$ as $n \to \infty$; thus

$$z_n \to \alpha \quad \text{but} \quad g(z_n) \nrightarrow g(\alpha),$$

and so g is discontinuous at α.

(b) We now show that $g(z) = z^{1/2}$ is continuous at 0 by using the ε-δ definition of continuity. We want to prove that for each $\varepsilon > 0$, there is $\delta > 0$ such that

$$z \in \mathbb{C}, |z - 0| < \delta \quad \Longrightarrow \quad \left| z^{1/2} - 0^{1/2} \right| < \varepsilon;$$

that is

$$|z| < \delta \quad \Longrightarrow \quad \left| z^{1/2} \right| < \varepsilon. \tag{$*$}$$

Now

$$\begin{aligned}
\left| z^{1/2} \right| < \varepsilon &\iff \left| z^{1/2} \right|^2 < \varepsilon^2 \\
&\iff |z| < \varepsilon^2.
\end{aligned}$$

Hence, with $\delta = \varepsilon^2$, the statement $(*)$ is satisfied and so g is continuous at 0.

Section 3

3.1 **(a)** The point $\alpha = 0$ is a limit point of
$A = \{z : |z| < 1\}$ because all points of the sequence
$$z_n = \frac{1}{n+1}, \quad n = 1, 2, \ldots,$$
lie in $A - \{0\}$ and $z_n \to 0$ as $n \to \infty$.

(b) The point $\alpha = i$ is a limit point of $A = \{z : \operatorname{Re} z > 0\}$
because all points of the sequence
$$z_n = \frac{1}{n} + i, \quad n = 1, 2, \ldots,$$
lie in $A - \{i\} = A$ and $z_n \to i$ as $n \to \infty$.

(c) The point $\alpha = 1$ is a limit point of $A = \{z : |z| = 1\}$
because all points of the sequence
$$z_n = e^{i\pi/n}, \quad n = 1, 2, \ldots,$$
lie in $A - \{1\}$ and $z_n \to 1$ as $n \to \infty$ (by the continuity of
the exponential function at 0).

(d) The point $\alpha = 2$ is a limit point of $A = \mathbb{C} - \{2\}$
because all the points of the sequence
$$z_n = 2 + \frac{1}{n}, \quad n = 1, 2, \ldots,$$
lie in $A - \{2\}$ ($= \mathbb{C} - \{2\}$) and $z_n \to 2$ as $n \to \infty$.

(e) The point $\alpha = -1$ is a limit point of $A = \mathbb{R} - \{-1\}$
because all points of the sequence
$$z_n = -1 + \frac{1}{n}, \quad n = 1, 2, \ldots,$$
lie in $A - \{-1\}$ ($= \mathbb{R} - \{-1\}$) and $z_n \to -1$ as $n \to \infty$.

3.2 First note that the domain of the function
$$f(z) = \frac{z^3 + i}{z - i}$$
is $\mathbb{C} - \{i\}$ and that i is a limit point of this set. Also
$$
\begin{aligned}
f(z) &= \frac{z^3 + i}{z - i} \\
&= \frac{(z - i)(z^2 + iz - 1)}{(z - i)} \\
&= z^2 + iz - 1, \quad \text{for } z \in \mathbb{C} - \{i\}.
\end{aligned}
$$
Thus, if $\{z_n\}$ is a sequence lying in $\mathbb{C} - \{i\}$ and $z_n \to i$,
then
$$
\begin{aligned}
f(z_n) &= z_n^2 + iz_n - 1 \\
&\to i^2 + i^2 - 1 = -3,
\end{aligned}
$$
by the Combination Rules for sequences, and so
$$\lim_{z \to i} \frac{z^3 + i}{z - i} = -3.$$

3.3 Let $f(z) = \dfrac{z}{\operatorname{Re} z}$. Then the domain of f is
$A = \{z : \operatorname{Re} z \neq 0\}$, and 0 is a limit point of A.
Consider the sequence
$$z_n = \frac{1}{n} + i\frac{k}{n}, \quad n = 1, 2, \ldots,$$
where $k \in \mathbb{N}$. Now $z_n \to 0$ through $A - \{0\}$, but
$$
\begin{aligned}
f(z_n) &= \left(\frac{1}{n} + i\frac{k}{n}\right) \bigg/ \frac{1}{n} \\
&= 1 + ik, \quad n = 1, 2, \ldots,
\end{aligned}
$$
so that
$$\lim_{n \to \infty} f(z_n) = 1 + ik.$$
Clearly, different values of k (e.g. 0 and 1) lead to
different limits, and so $\lim_{z \to 0} f(z)$ does not exist.

Alternatively, if
$$z_n = \frac{1}{n^2} + i\frac{1}{n}, \quad n = 1, 2, \ldots,$$
then
$$
\begin{aligned}
f(z_n) &= \left(\frac{1}{n^2} + i\frac{1}{n}\right) \bigg/ \frac{1}{n^2} \\
&= 1 + in, \quad n = 1, 2, \ldots
\end{aligned}
$$
so that $f(z_n) \to \infty$ as $n \to \infty$ and hence $\lim_{z \to 0} f(z)$ does
not exist.

3.4 **(a)** The function $f(z) = \exp(z^2 + 1)$ is continuous,
by the Composition Rule, and i is a limit point of $\mathbb{C}$, the
domain of f. Hence, by Theorem 3.1,
$$
\begin{aligned}
\lim_{z \to i} f(z) &= f(i) = \exp\left(i^2 + 1\right) \\
&= e^0 = 1.
\end{aligned}
$$

(b) The function $f(x) = e^{ix}$ is continuous on $\mathbb{R}$, by the
Composition Rule and Restriction Rule, and π is a limit
point of $\mathbb{R}$. Hence, by Theorem 3.1,
$$\lim_{x \to \pi} f(x) = f(\pi) = e^{i\pi} = -1.$$

3.5 Let $f(x) = \exp(i(x^2 - 1)/(x - 1))$. Then the domain
of f is $\mathbb{R} - \{1\}$ and 1 is a limit point of this set. Now
$$f(x) = \exp(i(x + 1)) \quad (x \in \mathbb{R} - \{1\}).$$
Thus, if $x_n \to 1$ ($x_n \neq 1$), then $i(x_n + 1) \to 2i$ and
$$
\begin{aligned}
f(x_n) &= \exp(i(x_n + 1)) \\
&\to e^{2i},
\end{aligned}
$$
by the continuity of the exponential function at $2i$. Hence
$$\lim_{x \to 1} \exp(i(x^2 - 1)/(x - 1)) = e^{2i}.$$

Section 4

4.1 **(a)** Let $A = \mathbb{C} - \{0\}$; then $\{0\}$ is the boundary of
A. If $\alpha \in A$, then the open disc $\{z : |z - \alpha| < |\alpha|\}$ lies
entirely in A, and so A is open.

(b) Let $A = \{z : -2 < \operatorname{Re} z < 2, -1 < \operatorname{Im} z < 1\}$ and
$\alpha \in A$. Then the distance from α to the boundary of A is
$$r_\alpha = \min\{2 - \operatorname{Re}\alpha, 1 - \operatorname{Im}\alpha, 2 + \operatorname{Re}\alpha, \operatorname{Im}\alpha + 1\} > 0.$$

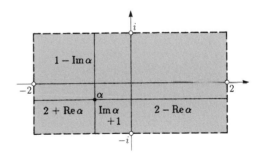

Thus the disc $\{z : |z - \alpha| < r_\alpha\}$ lies entirely in A, and
so A is open.

(c) Let $A = \{z : 1 < |z| < 2\}$ and $\alpha \in A$. Then the distance from α to the boundary of A is

$$r_\alpha = \min\{|\alpha| - 1, 2 - |\alpha|\} > 0.$$

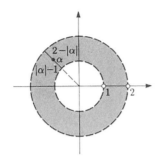

Thus the disc $\{z : |z - \alpha| < r_\alpha\}$ lies entirely in A, and so A is open.

(d) Let $A = \{z : \pi/3 < \text{Arg } z < 2\pi/3\}$ and $\alpha \in A$. The boundary of A is

$$\{0\} \cup \{z : \text{Arg } z = \pi/3\} \cup \{z : \text{Arg } z = 2\pi/3\},$$

and the distance from α to the boundary of A is

$$r_\alpha = \min\{d_1, d_2\} > 0,$$

where

$$d_1 = |\alpha| \sin(2\pi/3 - \text{Arg } \alpha), \quad d_2 = |\alpha| \sin(\text{Arg } \alpha - \pi/3).$$

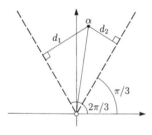

Thus the disc $\{z : |z - \alpha| < r_\alpha\}$ lies entirely in A, and so A is open.

4.2 **(a)** Each of the sets

$$A_1 = \{z : \text{Re } z > 0\}, \quad A_2 = \{z : \text{Im } z > 0\},$$
$$A_3 = \{z : |z| < 1\}$$

is open, and so

$$\{z : \text{Re } z > 0, \text{Im } z > 0, |z| < 1\} = A_1 \cap A_2 \cap A_3$$

is open, by the corollary to Theorem 4.1.

(b) Each of the sets

$$A_1 = \{z : \text{Re } z > 0\}, \quad A_2 = \{z : \text{Re } z < 0\}$$

is open, and so

$$\{z : \text{Re } z \neq 0\} = A_1 \cup A_2$$

is open, by Theorem 4.1(a).

4.3 **(a)** Let $A = \mathbb{C} - \{x \in \mathbb{R} : x \leq 0\}$. Then any two points α and β in A can be joined by a path in A of the type given in the solution to Example 4.2.

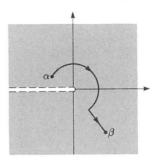

Alternatively, the points α and β can be joined by the path which is the union of the line segments from α to 1 and from 1 to β, for example, both of which lie in A.

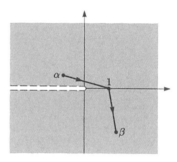

The set A is not convex because, for example, $-1 + i$ and $-1 - i$ cannot be joined by a line segment in A.

(b) If α and β lie in

$$A = \{z : -1 < \text{Re } z < 1 \text{ or } -1 < \text{Im } z < 1\},$$

then the line segments from α to 0 and from 0 to β both lie in A. Hence α can be joined to β in A by the path which is the union of these two line segments, as shown below.

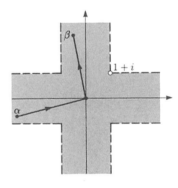

The set A is not convex because, for example, $2i$ and -3 cannot be joined by a line segment in A.

4.4 First choose a point α_0 in $A \cap B$ (possible since $A \cap B \neq \varnothing$). Now if α lies in A, then α can be joined to α_0 by a path Γ_α lying entirely in A, and hence in $A \cup B$. Similarly, if α lies in B, then α can be joined to α_0 by a path Γ_α lying entirely in B, and hence in $A \cup B$. Thus if α and β lie in $A \cup B$, then α and β can be joined by a path $\Gamma = \Gamma_\alpha \cup \Gamma_\beta$ lying entirely in $A \cup B$. Hence $A \cup B$ is connected.

4.5 Clearly, $\mathcal{R} \neq \varnothing$, since $0 \in \mathcal{R}$.

We now prove that $\mathcal{R}$ is open. Let $\alpha \in \mathcal{R}$.

If $|\operatorname{Im}\alpha| \neq 0$, then take $r_\alpha = |\operatorname{Im}\alpha|$ and note that
$$\{z : |z - \alpha| < r_\alpha\} \subseteq \mathcal{R}.$$

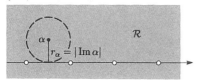

If $|\operatorname{Im}\alpha| = 0$, then α is real and
$$\left(n + \frac{1}{2}\right)\pi < \alpha < \left(n + 1 + \frac{1}{2}\right)\pi,$$
for some integer n. Thus, if
$$r_\alpha = \min\left\{\alpha - \left(n + \frac{1}{2}\right)\pi, \left(n + 1 + \frac{1}{2}\right)\pi - \alpha\right\},$$
then
$$\{z : |z - \alpha| < r_\alpha\} \subseteq \mathcal{R}.$$

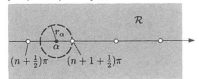

Hence $\mathcal{R}$ is open.

Next we prove that $\mathcal{R}$ is connected. (There are many ways of doing this.)

Any two points of $\mathcal{R}$ can be joined by a line segment, modified if necessary by semi-circular arcs to avoid points of $\mathbb{C} - \mathcal{R}$. At most a finite number of such points will need to be avoided. The figure shows some suitable paths formed in this way.

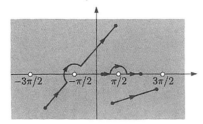

Section 5

5.1 **(a)** Since
$$\mathbb{C} - \{z : |z| \geq 1\} = \{z : |z| < 1\}$$
is open, we deduce that $\{z : |z| \geq 1\}$ is closed.

(b) Since
$$\mathbb{C} - \{z : |z| = 1\} = \{z : |z| < 1\} \cup \{z : |z| > 1\}$$
is open (by Theorem 4.1(a)), we deduce that $\{z : |z| = 1\}$ is closed.

5.2 **(a)** Each of the sets $E_1 = \{z : \operatorname{Re} z \leq 1\}$,
$E_2 = \{z : \operatorname{Re} z \geq -1\}$, $E_3 = \{z : \operatorname{Im} z \leq 1\}$,
$E_4 = \{z : \operatorname{Im} z \geq -1\}$, is a closed half-plane and hence
$$\{z : -1 \leq \operatorname{Re} z \leq 1, -1 \leq \operatorname{Im} z \leq 1\} = E_1 \cap E_2 \cap E_3 \cap E_4$$
is closed, by the corollary to Theorem 5.1.

(b) Each of the sets
$$E_1 = \{z : \operatorname{Im} z \geq 0\}, \quad E_2 = \{z : \operatorname{Im} z \leq 0\}$$
is a closed half-plane, and hence
$$\{z : \operatorname{Im} z = 0\} = E_1 \cap E_2,$$
is closed, by Theorem 5.1(b).

5.3 **(a)** The set $\{z : |z| = 1\}$ is closed, by Problem 5.1(b); it is bounded because it lies in the closed disc $\{z : |z| \leq 1\}$.

(b) The set $\{z : \operatorname{Im} z = 0\}$ is closed, by Problem 5.2(b); but it is not bounded.

(c) The set $E = \{z : -1 < \operatorname{Re} z < 1, -1 < \operatorname{Im} z < 1\}$ is bounded, since it lies in the closed disc $\{z : |z| \leq \sqrt{2}\}$. However, this set is not closed because its complement is not open. For example, the point 1 lies in $\mathbb{C} - E$, but no open disc centred at 1 lies entirely in $\mathbb{C} - E$, as indicated in the figure.

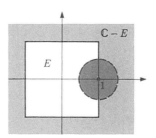

5.4 The set $A = \{z : -1 \leq \operatorname{Re} z \leq 1, -1 \leq \operatorname{Im} z \leq 1\}$ is closed, by Problem 5.2(a). It is bounded because it lies in the closed disc $\{z : |z| \leq \sqrt{2}\}$, for example. Hence A is compact.

5.5 **(a)** The function $f(z) = e^{1/z}$ is continuous on its domain $\mathbb{C} - \{0\}$, and hence on the circle $E = \{z : |z| = \frac{1}{2}\}$, which is a compact set. Hence f is bounded on E, by the Boundedness Theorem.

Alternatively,
$$\begin{aligned}
|f(z)| &= \left|e^{1/z}\right| \\
&\leq e^{|1/z|} \quad \text{(Problem 4.2(b) of } \textit{Unit A2}) \\
&= e^{1/|z|} \\
&= e^2, \quad \text{for } |z| = \tfrac{1}{2},
\end{aligned}$$
so that f is bounded on E.

(b) The function $f(z) = \sin z$ is continuous on $\mathbb{C}$ and hence on the closed disc $E = \{z : |z| \leq 27\}$, which is a compact set. Hence f is bounded on E, by the Boundedness Theorem.

Alternatively,
$$\begin{aligned}
|f(z)| &= |\sin z| \\
&= \left|\frac{e^{iz} - e^{-iz}}{2i}\right| \\
&\leq \frac{1}{2}\left(|e^{iz}| + |e^{-iz}|\right) \\
&\quad \text{(Triangle Inequality)} \\
&\leq \frac{1}{2}\left(e^{|z|} + e^{|z|}\right) \\
&\quad \text{(Problem 4.2(b) of } \textit{Unit A2} \text{ and } |iz| = |z|) \\
&= e^{|z|} \\
&\leq e^{27}, \quad \text{for } |z| \leq 27,
\end{aligned}$$
so that f is bounded on E.

(c) The function $f(z) = \left(z^2 + 1\right)/(z - 2i)$ is continuous on $\mathbb{C} - \{2i\}$, and hence on
$$E = \{z : -1 \leq \operatorname{Re} z \leq 1, -1 \leq \operatorname{Im} z \leq 1\},$$

which is a compact set (by Problem 5.4). Hence f is bounded on E, by the Boundedness Theorem.

Alternatively,

$$|f(z)| = \left| \frac{z^2 + 1}{z - 2i} \right|$$

$$\leq \frac{|z|^2 + 1}{||z| - 2|} \quad \text{(Triangle Inequality)}$$

$$\leq \frac{(\sqrt{2})^2 + 1}{|\sqrt{2} - 2|} \quad (\text{since } |z| \leq \sqrt{2}, \text{ for } z \in E)$$

$$= \frac{3}{2 - \sqrt{2}},$$

so that f is bounded on E.

5.6 **(a)** $\operatorname{int} A = \{z : |z| < 1\};$
    $\operatorname{ext} A = \{z : |z| > 1\};$
    $\partial A = \{z : |z| = 1\}.$

(b) $\operatorname{int} A = \{x + iy : x < 0\};$
    $\operatorname{ext} A = \{x + iy : x > 0\};$
    $\partial A = \{x + iy : x = 0\}.$

(c) $\operatorname{int} A = \mathbb{C} - \{0\};$
    $\operatorname{ext} A = \varnothing;$
    $\partial A = \{0\}.$

(d) $\operatorname{int} A = \varnothing;$
    $\operatorname{ext} A = \mathbb{C} - \{0\};$
    $\partial A = \{0\}.$

SOLUTIONS TO THE EXERCISES

Section 1

1.1 **(a)** To prove that the sequence $\{(1+i)/(2n^2 - 1)\}$ is null, we want to show that
for each positive number ε, there is an integer N such that

$$\left|\frac{1+i}{2n^2-1}\right| < \varepsilon, \quad \text{for all } n > N. \qquad (*)$$

Now $\left|\dfrac{1+i}{2n^2-1}\right| = \dfrac{|1+i|}{2n^2-1} = \dfrac{\sqrt{2}}{2n^2-1}$ for $n = 1, 2, \ldots$, so

$$\left|\frac{1+i}{2n^2-1}\right| < \varepsilon \iff \frac{\sqrt{2}}{2n^2-1} < \varepsilon$$

$$\iff n > \sqrt{\tfrac{1}{2}(\sqrt{2}/\varepsilon + 1)}.$$

Therefore, the statement $(*)$ holds if

$$N = \left[\sqrt{\tfrac{1}{2}(\sqrt{2}/\varepsilon + 1)}\right], \text{ and so } \{(1+i)/(2n^2-1)\} \text{ is a}$$

null sequence.

(b) If $z_n = (1+i)/(2n^2 - 1)$, then

$$|z_n| = \left|\frac{1+i}{2n^2-1}\right|$$

$$= \frac{\sqrt{2}}{2n^2-1}$$

$$\leq \frac{\sqrt{2}}{n^2}, \quad \text{for } n = 1, 2, \ldots,$$

as $2n^2 - 1 \geq n^2$ for $n = 1, 2, \ldots$.
Since $\{\sqrt{2}/n^2\}$ is a real null sequence of non-negative terms, it follows from the Squeeze Rule that $\{z_n\}$ is a null sequence.

1.2 **(a)** $\left\{\left(\dfrac{1}{2} + \dfrac{i}{2}\right)^n\right\}$ is a null sequence, by
Theorem 1.2, since it is of the form $\{\alpha^n\}$ where

$$|\alpha| = \left|\frac{1}{2} + \frac{i}{2}\right| = \frac{1}{\sqrt{2}} < 1.$$

(b) $\left\{\dfrac{1}{2} + \left(\dfrac{i}{2}\right)^n\right\}$ is *not* a null sequence. In fact, it has
limit $\frac{1}{2}$ since the sequence

$$z_n = \left(\frac{1}{2} + \left(\frac{i}{2}\right)^n\right) - \frac{1}{2}$$

$$= \left(\frac{i}{2}\right)^n, \quad n = 1, 2, \ldots,$$

is null, by Theorem 1.2. (See Remark 2 following the definition of a convergent sequence.)

(c) $\{(1+i)^n\}$ is *not* a null sequence. By Theorem 1.7, it tends to infinity, since it is of the form $\{\alpha^n\}$, where

$$|\alpha| = |1+i| = \sqrt{2} > 1.$$

1.3 **(a)** $\displaystyle\lim_{n\to\infty} \left(5 + \frac{i}{2n}\right) = \lim_{n\to\infty} 5 + \frac{i}{2}\lim_{n\to\infty}\frac{1}{n},$
by the Sum and Multiples Rules,
$$= 5 + 0 = 5.$$

(b) The dominant term in $z_n = (2n - i)/n^2$ is n^2, so we divide the numerator and denominator by it; hence

$$z_n = \frac{2n - i}{n^2}$$

$$= \frac{2n}{n^2} - \frac{i}{n^2}$$

$$= \frac{2}{n} - \frac{i}{n^2}.$$

Since $\{1/n\}$ and $\{1/n^2\}$ are basic null sequences,

$$\lim_{n\to\infty} z_n = (2 \times 0) - (i \times 0) = 0,$$

by the Sum and Multiple Rules.

(c) The dominant term in $z_n = (n - i)/(n + i)$ is n, so we divide the numerator and denominator by it; hence

$$z_n = \frac{n - i}{n + i}$$

$$= \frac{1 - i/n}{1 + i/n}.$$

Since $\{1/n\}$ is a basic null sequence,

$$\lim_{n\to\infty} z_n = \frac{1 - 0}{1 + 0} = 1,$$

by the Combination Rules.

(d) The dominant term in

$$z_n = (n^3 + 3in - 2)/(4n^3 - in^2)$$

is n^3, so we divide the numerator and denominator by it; hence

$$z_n = \frac{n^3 + 3in - 2}{4n^3 - in^2}$$

$$= \frac{1 + 3i/n^2 - 2/n^3}{4 - i/n}.$$

Since $\{1/n\}$, $\{1/n^2\}$ and $\{1/n^3\}$ are basic null sequences,

$$\lim_{n\to\infty} z_n = \frac{1 + 3i \times 0 - 2 \times 0}{4 - i \times 0} = \frac{1}{4},$$

by the Combination Rules.

(e) Since $|1+i| = \sqrt{2}$, $|\sqrt{3} - i| = 2$ and $|2 - 2i| = \sqrt{8}$, the dominant term in

$$z_n = \frac{(1+i)^n + (\sqrt{3} - i)^n}{3(2 - 2i)^n - 1}$$

is $(2 - 2i)^n$, so we divide the numerator and denominator by it. Thus

$$z_n = \frac{\left(\dfrac{1+i}{2 - 2i}\right)^n + \left(\dfrac{\sqrt{3} - i}{2 - 2i}\right)^n}{3 - 1/(2 - 2i)^n}.$$

Since

$$|(1 + i)/(2 - 2i)| = \sqrt{2}/\sqrt{8} = \tfrac{1}{2} < 1,$$

$$|(\sqrt{3} - i)/(2 - 2i)| = 2/\sqrt{8} = \frac{1}{\sqrt{2}} < 1$$

and

$$|1/(2 - 2i)| = 1/\sqrt{8} < 1,$$

$$\left\{\left(\frac{1+i}{2 - 2i}\right)^n\right\}, \left\{\left(\frac{\sqrt{3} - i}{2 - 2i}\right)^n\right\} \text{ and } \left\{\frac{1}{(2 - 2i)^n}\right\} \text{ are}$$

basic null sequences, by Theorem 1.2, and so

$$\lim_{n\to\infty} z_n = \frac{0 + 0}{3 - 0} = 0,$$

by the Combination Rules.

1.4 **(a)** Let $z_n = n/i$, for $n = 1, 2, \ldots$. Then

$$\frac{1}{z_n} = \frac{i}{n}.$$

Since $\{i/n\}$ is a null sequence (by Example 1.1), the sequence $\{n/i\}$ tends to infinity, by the Reciprocal Rule.

(b) Let $z_n = e^{in}$, for $n = 1, 2, \ldots$. Then

$$|z_n| = |e^{in}| = 1, \quad \text{for } n = 1, 2, \ldots.$$

Thus, for example, there is no integer N such that

$$|z_n| > 2, \quad \text{for all } n > N;$$

hence the definition of 'tends to infinity' does not hold with $M = 2$, and so the sequence $\{e^{in}\}$ does not tend to infinity.

(c) Let $z_n = ((\sqrt{3} - i)^n - 1)/(1 + i)^n$. Then
$$\frac{1}{z_n} = \frac{(1 + i)^n}{(\sqrt{3} - i)^n - 1}.$$
Since $|1 + i| = \sqrt{2}$ and $|\sqrt{3} - i| = 2$, the dominant term in $1/z_n$ is $(\sqrt{3} - i)^n$, so we divide the numerator and denominator by it. Thus
$$\frac{1}{z_n} = \frac{(1 + i)^n}{(\sqrt{3} - i)^n - 1}$$
$$= \frac{\left(\dfrac{1 + i}{\sqrt{3} - i}\right)^n}{1 - 1/(\sqrt{3} - i)^n}.$$
Since $|(1 + i)/(\sqrt{3} - i)| = \sqrt{2}/2 < 1$ and $|1/(\sqrt{3} - i)| = \frac{1}{2} < 1$, the sequences $\{((1 + i)/(\sqrt{3} - i))^n\}$ and $\{1/(\sqrt{3} - i)^n\}$ are null, by Theorem 1.2, and so
$$\lim_{n \to \infty} \frac{1}{z_n} = \frac{0}{1 - 0} = 0,$$
by the Combination Rules.

Hence $\{1/z_n\}$ is a null sequence, and so the sequence $\{z_n\}$ tends to infinity, by the Reciprocal Rule.

1.5 (a) Since $|i - 1| = \sqrt{2} > 1$, the sequence $\{(i - 1)^n\}$ is divergent, by Theorem 1.7(a).

(b) Since $e^{n\pi i} = (e^{\pi i})^n = (-1)^n$, the sequence $\{e^{n\pi i}\}$ is divergent, by Theorem 1.7(b).

(c) The subsequence $\{z_{4k}\}$ of the sequence
$$z_n = n \cos(n\pi i^n), \quad n = 1, 2, \ldots,$$
is
$$z_{4k} = 4k \cos(4k\pi i^{4k}), \quad k = 1, 2, \ldots.$$
Now
$$z_{4k} = 4k \cos(4k\pi) = 4k,$$
and so $\{z_{4k}\}$ tends to infinity (by the Reciprocal Rule: $1/(4k) \to 0$ as $k \to \infty$). Hence the sequence $\{z_n\}$ is divergent, by the Second Subsequence Rule.

1.6 To prove that
$$\lim_{n \to \infty} z_n = \alpha,$$
we must show that
for each positive number ε, there is an integer N such that
$$|z_n - \alpha| < \varepsilon, \quad \text{for all } n > N. \tag{1}$$
We know that $\{z_n\}$ consists of subsequences $\{z_{m_k}\}$ and $\{z_{n_k}\}$ which converge to α. Hence, there are integers K_1 and K_2 such that
$$|z_{m_k} - \alpha| < \varepsilon, \quad \text{for all } k > K_1, \tag{2}$$
and
$$|z_{n_k} - \alpha| < \varepsilon, \quad \text{for all } k > K_2. \tag{3}$$
From Inequalities (2) and (3), it follows that if we choose $N = \max\{m_{K_1}, n_{K_2}\}$, then Inequality (1) is satisfied. Hence
$$\lim_{n \to \infty} z_n = \alpha.$$

Section 2

2.1 (a) The function $f(z) = z^2$ is continuous at $\alpha = 2i$. We prove this as follows.

Let $\{z_n\}$ be any sequence (in $\mathbb{C}$, the domain of f) such that $z_n \to 2i$. We want to show that
$$z_n \to 2i \implies f(z_n) \to f(2i) = -4. \tag{$*$}$$
Now
$$f(z_n) = z_n^2$$
$$= z_n \times z_n$$
$$\to 2i \times 2i = -4,$$
by the Product Rule for sequences. Hence the statement $(*)$ holds, and proves that $f(z) = z^2$ is continuous at $2i$.

(b) The (principal cube root) function $f(z) = z^{1/3}$ has domain $\mathbb{C}$, which includes the point -1. We prove that $f(z) = z^{1/3}$ is discontinuous at -1, by finding a sequence $\{z_n\}$ such that
$$z_n \to -1 \quad \text{but} \quad f(z_n) \not\to f(-1).$$
Consider the sequence
$$z_n = e^{i(\pi + 1/n)}, \quad n = 1, 2, \ldots.$$
Then $z_n \to -1$ (see Problem 2.2, or use the continuity of $g(z) = \exp z$ at $i\pi$).

In terms of the principal argument,
$$z_n = e^{i(-\pi + 1/n)},$$
and so $|z_n| = 1$ and $\operatorname{Arg} z_n = -\pi + 1/n$. Thus
$$f(z_n) = z_n^{1/3}$$
$$= \exp\left(\tfrac{1}{3} \operatorname{Log} z_n\right)$$
$$= \exp(\log_e |z_n|^{1/3} + i(\operatorname{Arg} z_n)/3)$$
$$= \exp(\log_e 1) \exp(i(-\pi + 1/n)/3)$$
$$= \exp(-i\pi/3 + i/(3n)).$$
Now the sequence $\{-i\pi/3 + i/(3n)\}$ has limit $-i\pi/3$ (by the Sum and Multiple Rules), which is a point at which the function $g(z) = \exp z$ is continuous. Hence
$$f(z_n) = \exp(-i\pi/3 + i/(3n)) \to \exp(-i\pi/3)$$
$$= \frac{1}{2} - \frac{\sqrt{3}}{2}i.$$
But
$$f(-1) = (-1)^{1/3}$$
$$= \exp\left(\tfrac{1}{3} \operatorname{Log}(-1)\right)$$
$$= \exp(\log_e |-1|^{1/3} + i(\operatorname{Arg}(-1))/3)$$
$$= \exp(0 + i\pi/3)$$
$$= \frac{1}{2} + \frac{\sqrt{3}}{2}i$$
$$\neq \frac{1}{2} - \frac{\sqrt{3}}{2}i.$$
Hence
$$z_n \to -1 \quad \text{but} \quad f(z_n) \not\to f(-1),$$
and so f is discontinuous at -1.

2.2 **(a)** The functions $g(z) = 3z^3$, $h(z) = |z|$ and $k(z) = \operatorname{Re} z$ are basic continuous functions. By the Product Rule,

$$z \longmapsto |z| \operatorname{Re} z$$

is continuous, and hence

$$f(z) = 3z^3 + |z| \operatorname{Re} z$$

is continuous, by the Sum Rule.

(b) The functions $g(z) = |z|$ and $h(z) = \sin z$ are basic continuous functions. Hence, by the Composition Rule, the function

$$f(z) = g(h(z)) = |\sin z|$$

is continuous.

(c) The function $g(z) = 1 + z(i-1)$ is a polynomial function and, hence, continuous. The domain of g is $\mathbb{C}$, which contains the interval $[0,1]$, and hence the function

$$f(x) = 1 + x(i-1) \quad (x \in [0,1]),$$

which is the restriction of g to $[0,1]$, is continuous, by the Restriction Rule.

(d) The function $g(z) = e^{iz}$ is continuous (by the Composition Rule) and has domain $\mathbb{C}$, which contains the interval $[0, 2\pi]$. Hence

$$f(x) = \cos x + i \sin x \quad (x \in [0, 2\pi])$$

is continuous, by the Restriction Rule.

2.3 The domain of the function

$$f(z) = \theta,$$

where θ is the argument of z in the interval $[0, 2\pi[$, is $\mathbb{C} - \{0\}$.

To show that f is discontinuous at 1 we find a sequence $\{z_n\}$ in $\mathbb{C} - \{0\}$ such that

$$z_n \to 1 \quad \text{but} \quad f(z_n) \nrightarrow f(1).$$

Consider the sequence

$$z_n = e^{-i/n}, \quad n = 1, 2, \ldots,$$

which satisfies $z_n \to 1$, by the continuity of the exponential function at 0 (or by a geometric argument based on the following figure).

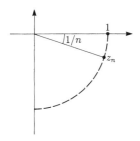

Now

$$f(z_n) = 2\pi - \frac{1}{n}, \quad n = 1, 2, \ldots,$$

so that

$$f(z_n) \to 2\pi \quad \text{(by the Combination Rules)}.$$

But $f(1) = 0$; hence $f(z_n) \nrightarrow f(1)$, and so f is discontinuous at 1.

In fact, the function f is discontinuous at each point of $\{x \in \mathbb{R} : x > 0\}$.

2.4 **(a)** The sequence

$$z_n = \pi + i/n, \quad n = 1, 2, \ldots,$$

has limit π, and π is a point at which the function $f(z) = \operatorname{Log} z$ is continuous. Hence

$$\lim_{n \to \infty} \operatorname{Log}(\pi + i/n) = \operatorname{Log} \pi$$
$$= \log_e \pi.$$

(b) Consider the sequence

$$z_n = \frac{(2n+1)\pi}{2n-1} i, \quad n = 1, 2, \ldots.$$

The dominant term in z_n is n, so we divide the numerator and denominator by n, giving

$$z_n = \frac{(2 + 1/n)\pi}{2 - 1/n} i;$$

hence, by the Combination Rules,

$$z_n \to \pi i.$$

The function $f(z) = \exp z$ is continuous at πi; hence

$$\lim_{n \to \infty} \exp\left(\frac{(2n+1)\pi}{2n-1} i\right) = \exp(\pi i)$$
$$= -1.$$

(c) Consider the sequence

$$z_n = \frac{(1+i)^n}{(2+i)^n}, \quad n = 1, 2, \ldots.$$

Since $|(1+i)/(2+i)| = \sqrt{2}/\sqrt{5} < 1$, $\{z_n\}$ is a basic null sequence (Theorem 1.2). The function $f(z) = \cos z$ is continuous at 0; hence

$$\lim_{n \to \infty} \cos\left(\frac{(1+i)^n}{(2+i)^n}\right) = \cos(0) = 1.$$

Section 3

3.1 **(a)** The point i is a limit point of $A = \{z : |z| < 1\}$.

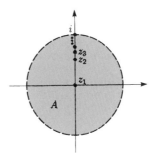

The sequence

$$z_n = \left(1 - \frac{1}{n}\right) i, \quad n = 1, 2, \ldots$$

lies in $A - \{i\} = A$, and

$$z_n \to i,$$

by the Sum and Multiple Rules. Hence i is a limit point of A.

(b) The point i is not a limit point of $A = \{z : \operatorname{Re} z > 1\}$.

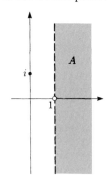

(c) The point 1 is a limit point of $A = \{z : \operatorname{Re} z + \operatorname{Im} z = 1\}$.

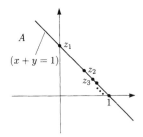

The sequence
$$z_n = \left(1 - \frac{1}{n}\right) + \frac{i}{n}, \quad n = 1, 2, \ldots,$$
lies in $A - \{1\}$, and
$$z_n \to 1,$$
by the Sum and Multiple Rules. Hence 1 is a limit point of A.

3.2 **(a)** The domain of the function
$$f(z) = \frac{z^3 - 27}{z - 3}$$
is $\mathbb{C} - \{3\}$ and 3 is a limit point of this set. Also,
$$f(z) = \frac{z^3 - 27}{z - 3} = z^2 + 3z + 9, \quad \text{for } z \in \mathbb{C} - \{3\}.$$
Thus, if $\{z_n\}$ is any sequence lying in $\mathbb{C} - \{3\}$ and $z_n \to 3$, then
$$f(z_n) = z_n^2 + 3z_n + 9$$
$$\to 3^2 + (3 \times 3) + 9 = 27,$$
by the Combination Rules for sequences. Hence
$$\lim_{z \to 3} \frac{z^3 - 27}{z - 3} = 27.$$

(b) The domain of the function
$$f(z) = \frac{z^2 + 1}{z + i}$$
is $\mathbb{C} - \{-i\}$ and $-i$ is a limit point of this set. Also,
$$f(z) = \frac{z^2 + 1}{z + i} = z - i, \quad \text{for } z \in \mathbb{C} - \{-i\}.$$
Thus, if $\{z_n\}$ is any sequence lying in $\mathbb{C} - \{-i\}$ and $z_n \to -i$, then
$$f(z_n) = z_n - i$$
$$\to -i - i = -2i,$$
by the Sum Rule for sequences. Hence
$$\lim_{z \to -i} \frac{z^2 + 1}{z + i} = -2i.$$

(c) The functions $g(z) = e^z$, $h(z) = \sinh z$ and $k(z) = 1/z$ are basic continuous functions. Hence, by the Product and Sum Rules, the function
$$f(z) = e^z \sinh z + 1/z$$
is continuous (on $\mathbb{C} - \{0\}$). In particular, f is continuous at $i\pi$, a limit point of $\mathbb{C} - \{0\}$. Hence, by Theorem 3.1,
$$\lim_{z \to i\pi} f(z) = f(i\pi)$$
$$= e^{i\pi} \sinh(i\pi) + \frac{1}{i\pi}$$
$$= (-1) \times (i \sin \pi) - \frac{i}{\pi} = -\frac{i}{\pi}.$$

(d) It follows from Theorem 3.1 that
$$\lim_{z \to 1} \operatorname{Im} z = \operatorname{Im} 1 = 0,$$
so it looks as if $\lim_{z \to 1}(1/\operatorname{Im} z)$ does not exist.

The domain of the function $f(z) = 1/\operatorname{Im} z$ is $A = \mathbb{C} - \{z : \operatorname{Im} z = 0\}$; that is, $\mathbb{C}$ with the real axis removed. Also, 1 is a limit point of A; for example, the sequence $\{1 + i/n\}$ lies in $A - \{1\}$ and $1 + i/n \to 1$ as $n \to \infty$. However
$$f(1 + i/n) = \frac{1}{\operatorname{Im}(1 + i/n)} = n,$$
and so tends to infinity. Hence $f(z) = 1/\operatorname{Im} z$ does not have a limit as z tends to 1.

(e) The functions $f(z) = \operatorname{Re} z$ and $g(z) = \operatorname{Im} z$ are continuous on $\mathbb{C}$, and so f/g is continuous on
$$\mathbb{C} - \{z : \operatorname{Im} z = 0\} = \mathbb{C} - \mathbb{R}.$$
Since $\operatorname{Im} i = 1 \neq 0$, we deduce that
$$\lim_{z \to i} \frac{\operatorname{Re} z}{\operatorname{Im} z} = \frac{\operatorname{Re} i}{\operatorname{Im} i} = 0,$$
by Theorem 3.1.

(f) Since $\lim_{z \to 0} \operatorname{Re} z = 0$ and $\lim_{z \to 0} \operatorname{Im} z = 0$ (by Theorem 3.1), it looks as if $\lim_{z \to 0} \dfrac{\operatorname{Re} z}{\operatorname{Im} z}$ may not exist. The function $f(z) = \dfrac{\operatorname{Re} z}{\operatorname{Im} z}$ has domain $A = \{z : \operatorname{Im} z \neq 0\}$ and 0 is a limit point of A.

Consider the sequence
$$z_n = \frac{1}{n} + i\frac{k}{n}, \quad n = 1, 2, \ldots,$$
where $k \in \mathbb{N}$. Now $z_n \to 0$ through $A - \{0\}$, but
$$f(z_n) = \frac{\operatorname{Re}((1 + ki)/n)}{\operatorname{Im}((1 + ki)/n)}$$
$$= \frac{1/n}{k/n}$$
$$= 1/k,$$
so that $f(z_n) \to 1/k$ as $n \to \infty$. Clearly, different values of k lead to different limits, and so $\lim_{z \to 0} f(z)$ does not exist.

3.3 Let $\{z_n\}$ be any sequence in $\mathbb{C} - \{0\}$ such that $z_n \to 0$. Then, since
$$\frac{(z + 2)^2 - (4 + z)}{z} = \frac{z^2 + 3z}{z}$$
$$= z + 3, \quad \text{for } z \neq 0,$$
the sequence $\left\{ \dfrac{(z_n + 2)^2 - (4 + z_n)}{z_n} \right\}$ has limit 3. Hence, since the cosine function is continuous at the point 3,
$$\lim_{z \to 0} \cos\left(\frac{(z + 2)^2 - (4 + z)}{z} \right) = \cos 3.$$

Section 4

4.1 (a)

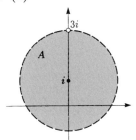

$A = \{z : |z - i| < 2\}$ is
open,
convex,
connected,
a region.

(b)

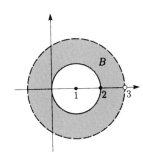

$B = \{z : 1 \le |z - 1| < 2\}$ is
not open,
not convex,
connected,
not a region.

(c)

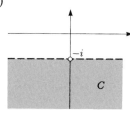

$C = \{z : \operatorname{Im} z < -1\}$ is
open,
convex,
connected,
a region.

(d) $A \cap C = \varnothing$ is

$\left.\begin{array}{l} \text{open} \\ \text{convex} \\ \text{connected} \end{array}\right\}$ (There are no points at which the definitions fail!)

not a region (a region must be non-empty).

(e)

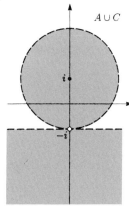

$A \cup C$ is
open,
not convex,
not connected
(no path in $A \cup C$
joins 0 and $-2i$,
for example),
not a region.

(f)

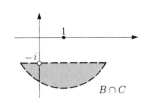

$B \cap C$ is
open,
convex,
connected,
a region.

(g)

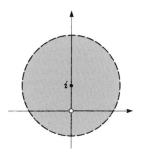

$A - \{0\}$ is
open,
not convex,
connected,
a region (by Theorem 4.3)

4.2 We prove that $A = \{z : |z - i| < 2\}$ is (a) open, (b) convex, (c) connected, (d) a region.

(a) The boundary of A is $\{z : |z - i| = 2\}$. If $\alpha \in A$, then the distance from α to the boundary of A is

$$r_\alpha = 2 - |\alpha - i| > 0.$$

Hence the open disc

$$\{z : |z - \alpha| < r_\alpha\}$$

lies entirely in A (see the figure), so that A is open.

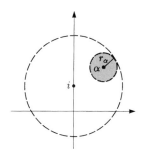

(b) Let α and β be any two points of A. Clearly the line segment from α to β lies entirely within A. Hence A is convex.

(c) Since A is convex, A is connected.

(d) A is non-empty (it contains the point i, for example), open and connected; hence it is a region.

4.3 The domain of the function $f(z) = \operatorname{cosec} z$ is

$$\mathcal{R} = \mathbb{C} - \{n\pi : n \in \mathbb{Z}\}.$$

Clearly $\mathcal{R}$ is non-empty since, for example, $\pi/2 \in \mathcal{R}$.

We now prove that $\mathcal{R}$ is open. Let $\alpha \in \mathcal{R}$.

If $|\operatorname{Im} \alpha| \ne 0$, then take $r_\alpha = |\operatorname{Im} \alpha|$ and note that

$$\{z : |z - \alpha| < r_\alpha\} \subseteq \mathcal{R},$$

as illustrated.

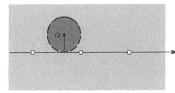

If $|\operatorname{Im}\alpha| = 0$, then α is real and
$$n\pi < \alpha < (n+1)\pi,$$
for some integer n. Thus, if
$$r_\alpha = \min\{\alpha - n\pi, (n+1)\pi - \alpha\},$$
then
$$\{z : |z - \alpha| < r_\alpha\} \subseteq \mathcal{R},$$
as illustrated.

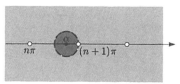

Hence $\mathcal{R}$ is open.

Next we prove that $\mathcal{R}$ is connected. (There are many ways of doing this.)

Any two points of $\mathcal{R}$ can be joined by a line segment, modified if necessary by semi-circular arcs to avoid points of $\mathbb{C} - \mathcal{R}$. At most, a finite number of such points will need to be avoided. The figure shows some suitable paths formed in this way.

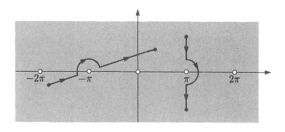

Section 5

5.1 The sets $A, B, A \cap C, B \cap C$ and $A - \{0\}$ are bounded, for each is contained in the closed disc $\{z : |z| \le 3\}$. (Note that $A \cap C = \varnothing$ is contained in every set.)

5.2 (a) The complement of $E = \{z : |z - i| \ge 2\}$ is $\{z : |z - i| < 2\}$, which is open, by Exercise 4.2(a). Hence E is a closed set.

(b) The complement of $E = \{z : |z - 1| < 1$ or $|z - 1| \ge 2\}$ is $\{z : 1 \le |z - 1| < 2\}$, which is not open. Hence E is not a closed set.

(c) The complement of $E = \{z : \operatorname{Im} z \le -1\}$ is $\{z : \operatorname{Im} z > -1\}$, which is open. Hence E is a closed set.

5.3 (a) The function $f(z) = \sinh z$ is continuous on its domain $\mathbb{C}$ and hence on $E = \{z : |z| \le 1\}$, which is a compact set. So f is bounded on E, by Theorem 5.3.

(b) Theorem 5.3 is inapplicable because the function $f(z) = \operatorname{Log} z$ is not defined at 0, which is in $E = \{z : |z| \le 1\}$, and so is not continuous on E.

(c) Theorem 5.3 is inapplicable because $E = \{z : \operatorname{Re} z \ge 1\}$ is not a compact set (it is not bounded).

(d) The function $f(z) = 1/z$ is continuous on its domain $\mathbb{C} - \{0\}$ and hence continuous on $E = \{z : 1 \le |z| \le 2\}$, which is a compact set. So f is bounded on E, by Theorem 5.3.

(e) Theorem 5.3 is inapplicable because $E = \{z : 0 < |z| \le 2\}$ is not a compact set (it is not closed).

(f) Theorem 5.3 is inapplicable because $E = \{z : |z| \ge 1\}$ is not a compact set (it is not bounded). However, note that f is actually bounded (by 1) on E.

5.4 $\operatorname{int} A = \{z : |z - 1| < 1$ or $|z - 1| > 2\}$;
$\operatorname{ext} A = \{z : 1 < |z - 1| < 2\}$;
$\partial A = \{z : |z - 1| = 1$ or $|z - 1| = 2\}$.